CNC PART PROGRAMMING

David Gibbs
T. Eng., MIED
Senior Lecturer in the Department of Technology
Reading College of Technology

Cassell

Cassell Publishers Limited
Artillery House
Artillery Row
London SW1P 1RT

British Library Cataloguing in Publication Data

Gibbs, David
  CNC part programming.—(Cassell computing).
  1. Machine-tools—Numerical control
  I. Title
  621.9'023   TJ1189

ISBN 0-304-31355-6

Photoset by Multiplex medway ltd, Walderslade.
Printed and bound in Great Britain by Mackays of Chatham

Last digit is print no: 9 8 7 6 5 4 3 2 1

CONTENTS

PREFACE

This book is intended to support the essentially practical activity of preparing and proving CNC part programs. It will be of value to students on a wide range of courses, including published courses such as the City and Guilds of London Institute 230 Series in CNC Part Programming and CNC Advanced Part Programming, various BTEC Units and the many short courses that are run both by colleges and industrial organisations.

The preparation and proving of CNC part programs requires access to machinery and computer installations in order to obtain the necessary practical experience. Using such equipment, and understanding particular programming languages and techniques, requires instruction and tuition from a competent tutor. Students undertaking a course of study devoted to part programming will, therefore, find it necessary to attend an adequately resourced college or training centre. The intending student must also have a good understanding of CNC machining techniques, and should ideally have previous experience of completing simple CNC part programs. In preparing this text these fundamental requirements have been borne in mind.

CNC part programming is an absorbing and time-consuming activity—it is one of the few areas of study where students complain that time has passed too quickly! Thus a primary objective of this book is to ensure that limited course time can be used to the best advantage by providing the opportunity to devote as much time as possible to preparing programs and using the associated equipment. Accordingly, an attempt has been made to include sufficient information to provide the student with much of the theoretical knowledge needed to support the more practical elements of study, so reducing the time spent on formal lectures and unnecessary note taking. The text also provides the student with the opportunity to study specific aspects of interest as and when it suits him or her to do so.

The text is essentially practical in nature and is intended to provide adequate material for course work. It contains a series of assignments which will provide the student with a practical understanding of the equipment he or she will be using. Throughout the book there are numerous fully detailed drawings of components which, while primarily included to complement the text, may also be used as programming exercises in the early stages of a course. An additional series of projects, of varying degrees of complexity and intended for later use, should satisfy most levels of ability.

It is the author's experience that many mature people returning to college for re-training, and also many younger students, are hampered in their programming work by a lack of ability to perform relatively simple calculations. It is generally outside the scope of a course of study devoted to part programming to spend much time rectifying this state of affairs, and yet it cannot be ignored. To assist both tutors and students there is a chapter devoted entirely to the type of calculations that will be encountered when preparing part programs manually; it is hoped that the completion of these exercises, supported by on-the-spot tuition, will be of value.

This book is intended to serve as a companion volume to *An Introduction to CNC Machining* and as such it is similarly directed at the common machine-shop engineering processes of turning, milling and drilling.

D.A.W. Gibbs
Wokingham 1987

ACKNOWLEDGEMENTS

The author and publisher would like to thank the following organisations who have contributed material for inclusion in this book:

Anderson Strathclyde PLC

Camtek Ltd

Guhring Ltd

Hardinge Machine Tools Ltd

Hebard (South West) Ltd

Kongsberg Systems Technology Ltd

Mills Marketing Services Ltd

Stellram Ltd

1

PART PROGRAMMING: TECHNIQUES, TERMS AND DEFINITIONS

The part program

The term 'part program' is used to describe a set of instructions which, when entered into a machine control unit, will cause the machine to function in the manner necessary to produce a particular component or part.

The program may be prepared manually and expressed in a coded language that is applicable to the machine controller being used. Alternatively it may be written in another language or compiled by the use of computer graphics. The result is then post-processed, or translated, to suit the machine controller.

Included in the part program will be the necessary dimensional data relating to the features of the component itself, together with control data that will result in the machine making the slide movements required to produce the component. These data will be supplemented by data that will activate and control the appropriate supporting functions.

Programs as entered into machine control units involve either of two programming concepts:

(a) conversational manual data input (MDI);
(b) word address.

There are considerable variations between the two methods.

Conversational part programming

Conversational part programming requires the programmer to respond to a set of options that is a built-in feature of the machine control system and displayed on the VDU screen of the control unit. As each response is made, further options are presented and responses made until that particular group, or 'block' of related data is complete. The programmer then moves on to the next block.

For example, assume that, as part of a milling program, a relative tool movement of -39.786 mm is required in a certain direction identified as the X

axis. An appropriate feed rate has already been programmed.

With conversational programming the programmer will establish the appropriate operating mode, that is, linear motion at a controlled feed rate, by making a selection from a list of alternatives. That selection having been made, the next prompt will ask for the dimensional value of the intended move in the *X* axis.

If listed, the data for the above move would read:

N260 MILL X-39.786

where the entry MILL indicates the type of slide movement required and N260 is the data block number.

Similarly, consider a program entry to achieve combined slide movements that will result in a cutter path passing through an arc of 90° and having a radius of 8 mm.

First, the appropriate operating mode will be selected, such as CIRC—an abbreviation for circular interpolation. The prompts which follow will ask for the target position in the respective axes followed by the value of the radius and the direction of movement, whether clockwise or counter-clockwise.

A listed program block containing these data would read

N350 CIRC X43.765 Z-75.000 R8 CW

The conversational concept can be extended to include machining requirements other than slide movement control.

Consider the turning of a bar of metal on a turning centre. Before any thought can be given to slide movements, the basic metal-cutting data would have to be ascertained. For example, the correct spindle speed and feed rate are of vital importance. The spindle speed is affected by the work diameter and the cutting speed. The cutting speed is related to the material being machined. The feed rate would depend on the depth of cut, tool type and surface finish required.

From this it can be seen that the necessary data to machine the metal successfully can be related to four factors:

(a) the material being cut;
(b) the material diameter;
(c) the surface finish required;
(d) the tool type.

The computer will be programmed to select the appropriate spindle speed and feed rate from an input of information relating to these factors. To assist the input of information there will be a material file and surface roughness file within the computer memory, as shown in Figure 1.1. Cutting tool types will also be numerically identified.

A simple question-and-answer routine will extract from the computer memory all the necessary data to give the correct cutting conditions, making calculations or judgements on the part of the programmer quite unnecessary.

An example of a question-and-answer routine is as follows:

Prompt	*Response*
Material?	5 input
Material diameter?	50 input
Surface code?	4 input
Tool number?	8 input

MATERIAL STOCK FILE	
CODE	MATERIAL
1	MILD STEEL
2	MED. CARBON STEEL
3	STAINLESS STEEL
4	CAST IRON
5	DURALUMIN

SURFACE ROUGHNESS FILE	
CODE	Ra
1	100
2	50
3	25
4	12.5
5	6.3

Figure 1.1   *Material file and surface roughness file.*

There is no standard conversational part programming language. The systems are very individualistic. It should also be noted that while conversational MDI programs can be prepared away from the machine and then instantly entered into the control,   usually by the use of magnetic tape, they are commonly entered by the machine setter/operator pressing appropriate buttons as described above. Unless the machine control unit is of the less common type that permits a second program to be entered while the first is being activated, shop floor data entry involves the machine being non-productive while the program is being entered, and this does have its drawbacks. On the other hand, the technique is favoured by some companies since total control of the machining operation by workshop personnel (as opposed to programs being prepared away from the shop floor and then subsequently passed on to them), makes use of valuable practical skills and, equally important, has the effect of improving job satisfaction.

Word address programming

Word address programming is largely based on an International Standards Organisation (ISO) code, now withdrawn, which requires the program to be compiled using codes identified by letters, in particular G and M. Each code addresses, or directs, the item of data it precedes to perform a certain function within the control system.

The ISO Standard provided for 99 G codes and an identical number of M codes, each being expressed by the address letter followed by two digits.

Not all the codes were allocated a specific function in the Standard and this gave the manufacturers of control systems the opportunity to introduce their own variations. There is, therefore, no standard word address machine programming language, although many of the recommendations made have been widely adopted.

The G codes, or preparatory functions, are used to inform the machine control unit of the facilities required for the machining that is to be carried out— whether movement is to be in a straight line or radially, for example. In general they relate to slide motion control. Examples of commonly used G codes are as follows:

G00	Rapid positioning, point to point
G01	Positioning at a controlled feed rate
G02	Circular interpolation, clockwise
G03	Circular interpolation, counter-clockwise
G04	Dwell for programmed duration
G33	Thread cutting, constant lead
G34	Thread cutting, increasing lead
G40	Cutter compensation, cancel
G41	Cutter compensation, left
G42	Cutter compensation, right
G53	Linear shift, cancel
G54	Linear shift
G55	Linear shift
G80	Series associated with drilling, boring, tapping and reaming.

G codes may be 'modal', that is, they remain active until cancelled. Alternatively they may be non-modal, and only operative for the block in which they are programmed.

The M codes, or miscellaneous functions, are used to establish requirements other than those related to slide movement. For example, they are used to activate spindle motion or to turn on a coolant supply. Examples of commonly used M codes are as follows:

M00	Program stop
M01	Optional stop
M02	End of program
M03	Spindle on clockwise
M04	Spindle on counter-clockwise
M05	Spindle off
M06	Tool change
M08	Coolant on
M09	Coolant off
M30	End of tape

As with G codes, some M functions are modal, remaining active until cancelled.

In addition to the address letters G and M there is also common usage of S, F and T to indicate speeds, feeds and tooling. The letter N is always used to identify block numbers.

The distinction between word address and conversational programming is best appreciated by reference to the simple movements discussed earlier.

To program the linear movement of −39.786 in the X axis using the word address technique, it is first necessary to establish the operating mode required. This is done by including the appropriate G code, in this case G01. Thus the complete program entry for the required move will be:

N260 G01 X-39.786

Similarly, reconsider the 8 mm radial movement through an arc of 90°. Once again the mode of operation has to be established using the appropriate G code, which for circular movement in a clockwise direction is G02. It will also be necessary to define the target position in the appropriate axes and also the start of the arc in relation to the arc centre using I, J and K address letters that correspond to the X, Y and Z axes respectively. A word address program entry to achieve this movement would read as follows:

N350 G02 X43.765 Z-75.000 K8

There are variations in procedure even when word address programming such a common machining feature as a radius. On some control systems the arc centre may have to be defined—still using the I, J and K address letters—in relation to the program datum and not the start position.

The programming of radial movements using the word address method will be returned to later in the text.

A word address program that includes a number of codes is listed below. The program relates to the component detailed in Figure 1.2, and is typical of its type. The comments written alongside the data should convey to the reader an impression of how, prior to programming, the machining of a component is first broken down into operations. It also shows how the necessary machine control data is presented. Later in the text further reference will be made to the program to illustrate specific programming techniques and features.

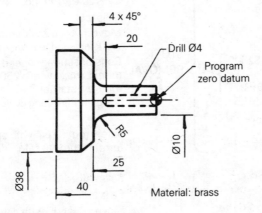

Figure 1.2 *Component detail.*

MACHINE: HARDINGE HXL TURNING CENTRE CONTROL: GE 1050
SAMPLE PROGRAM FOR DRAWING FIGURE 1.2

N0010	G71		Metric
N0020	G40		Cancels Tool Nose Radius compensation (TNRC)
N0030	G95	SAFETY ROUTINE	Feed mm/rev
N0040	G97 S1000 M03		Spindle rev/min, CW
N0050	G00		Cancels G01, G02, G03, etc.
N0060	G53 X 177.8 Z254 T00		Return to safe indexing position, offsets cancelled
N0070	M01		Optional stop

N0100	G25 $P_1$10 $P_2$60		Calls safety routine
N0110	T1200		Calls tool
N0120	G54 X0 Z3 T1212	CENTRE DRILL	Move in X and Y with zero shift to work face and tool offset active
N0130	S2500 F.1		Spindle speed and feed
N0140	G01 Z-6		Centre drill
N0150	G00 Z2		Drill retract
N0160	G25 $P_1$10 $P_2$70		Safety routine call with optional stop, turret returns to safe indexing position

N0200	G25 $P_1$10 $P_2$60		Calls safety routine
N0210	T1400		Calls tool
N0220	G54 X0 Z3 T1414	PECK DRILL CYCLE	Move in X and Z with zero shift to work face and tool offset active
N0230	S2000 F.15		Spindle speed and feed
N0240	G83 Z-20 $P_1$10 P_2.8 $P_5$4		Peck drill cycle
N0250	G25 $P_1$10 $P_2$70		Safety routine call with optional stop, turret returns to safe indexing position

N0300	G25 $P_1$10 $P_2$60		Calls safety routine
N0310	T400		Calls tool
N0320	G54 X44 Z2.5 T404	STOCK REMOVAL CYCLE	Move in X and Z with zero shift to work face and tool offset active
N0330	G92 R44 S2500		Constant surface speed of 250 m/min, max rev/min 2500, feed .15 mm/rev, start at Ø44
N0340	G96 S250 F15		
N0350	G68 X10 Z0 I.5 K.5 $P_1$900 $P_2$930 $P_3$1.5 P_4-0		Roughing/finishing cycle
N0360	G25 $P_1$10 $P_2$70		Safety routine call with optional stop, turret returns to safe indexing position

N0400	G25 $P_1$10 $P_2$60	(PART OFF)	Calls safety routine
N0410	T300		Calls tool
N0420	G54 X44 Z-40 T303		Move in X and Z with zero shift to work face, tool offset active

N0430	G92 R44 S2000 ⎫		Constant surface speed of 200 m/min, max rev/min 2000, start at Ø44, feed .05 mm/rev.
N0440	G96 S200 F.05 ⎭		
N0450	G01 X0	(PART	Part off
N0460	G00 X48	OFF)	Rapid withdraw
N0470	G25 $P_1$10 $P_2$70		Safety routine call with option stop, turret returns to safe indexing position
N0480	M30		Program end, rewind, coolant off
N0900	G64 Z-25 $P_1$5	PROFILE	Cycle for Z axis move followed by 90° radius
N0910	G63 X38 P_1-45 $P_2$4	DATA	Cycle for X axis move followed by chamfer
N0920	GOI Z-40		Z axis move
N0930	X44		X axis move

Note: N0900 - N0930 defines the profile called in the roughing/finishing cycle G68 at block N0350

Data format

Data is written in blocks. The data within a block must be expressed either in a fixed sequence with each block containing all data (even if it has not changed from the previous block) or, more commonly, in random order without the repetition of unchanged data but with each word being clearly identified by its address letter. The terminology used to describe these two methods is 'fixed block' and 'variable block' respectively.

It is necessary for the part programmer to be aware of the data format for the system being used, and also to be familiar with the classification of the data which dictates the way in which it may be presented within a block. For example, a programming manual could indicate that data must conform to the following classification:

N4, G2, X3/3, Y3/3, Z3/3, F3, S4, T2, M2

This classification indicates the following:

N4	The block sequence address letter N may be followed by up to four digits.
G2	The preparatory function address letter G may be followed by up to two digits.
X3/3, Y3/3, Z3/3	The axis identification letters X, Y and Z may be followed by up to three digits in front of the decimal point, and up to three after. (Dimensional values may be subject to other limitations as explained below.)
F3	The feed address letter F may be followed by up to three digits.
S4	The spindle speed or cutting speed address letter S may be followed by up to four digits.

T2	The tool address letter T may be followed by up to two digits.
M2	The miscellaneous function address letter M may be followed by up to two digits.

The description above has stated that up to so many digits may be used. Some systems require that leading zeros are included. Thus a linear slide movement at a programmed feed rate may be programmed as G01 or G1.

Similarly, dimensional values may also have to be programmed according to certain rules. For instance, using a data classification of 3/3 it would be possible, depending on the requirements of the system, to program a value of 32 mm in a number of ways:

(a) 032000—all digits must be included but no decimal point.
(b) 32000—leading zeros are omitted, but no decimal point is required; trailing zeros must be included.
(c) 32.000—the decimal point and all trailing zeros are required.
(d) 32.—no leading or trailing zeros are required but the decimal point must be included.
(e) 32—whole numbers may be programmed without leading or trailing zeros and without a decimal point.

Slide movements

Both word address and conversational programming require definition of the slide movements necessary to position the cutting tool correctly in relation to the work.

This positioning is described in three ways:

(a) point-to-point;
(b) line motion;
(c) contouring.

Point-to-point positioning involves programming instructions which identify only the next relative tool position required. The position may be reached by movement in one or more axes at a rate of travel which is generally, though not necessarily, the maximum for the machine. No metal cutting takes place during the positioning moves.

Figure 1.3 shows details of a component. To drill the holes in this component would require point-to-point positioning. Note that it is the positioning prior to drilling that is point-to-point, not the drilling operation itself.

Line motion control requires programmed instructions that specify both the next position and the rate of travel, or feed rate, to be employed to reach that position; the resulting cutter path is a straight line. Metal cutting would normally take place during such a move. Line motion control is also referred to as 'linear interpolation'. Figure 1.4 illustrates an example of line motion control.

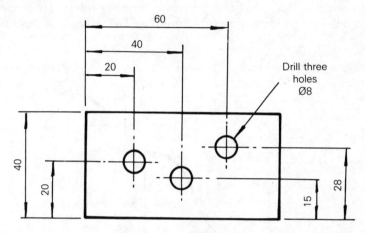

Figure 1.3 *Component detail requiring point-to-point positioning to drill holes.*

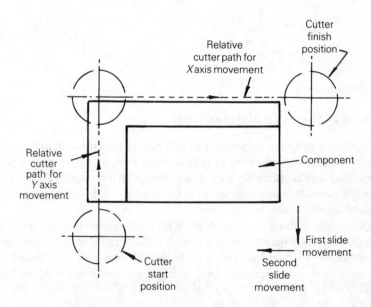

Figure 1.4 *Line motion control (linear interpolation).*

Contouring is used to describe movements involving at least two slides. The movements occur simultaneously and at a predetermined feed rate, and result in a continuous machining path which is not a straight line. An elliptical profile or a combination of arcs—the production of an arc being referred to as 'circular interpolation'—are good examples of contouring. The principle is illustrated in Figure 1.5.

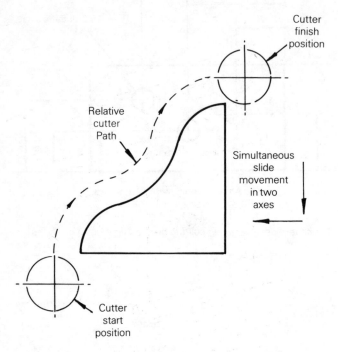

Figure 1.5 *Contouring*

Definition of the axes of movement

Whether conversational or word address programming is being used, the direction in which slide movement is to occur is defined by a letter, which for common machines is either X, Y or Z, together with a positive (+) or negative (−) sign. In practice the + sign is not actually entered, for if a sign is omitted the control automatically assumes plus.

The definition of the axes of movement on common machine types, namely a turning centre, a vertical machining centre and a horizontal machining centre, are illustrated in Figure 1.6. Two points should be noted in relation to the illustrations. First, on a turning centre having a rear-mounted tool post the plus (+) and minus (−) in the X axis would be reversed. Movement of the tool away from the spindle axis is always plus.

Second, the axes definitions shown indicate the *machine* slide movements. In the case of a turning centre these movements are identical to the tool movement in relation to the work. On milling machines, where it is the table and not the cutting tool which moves, this is not the case. For programming purposes, where it is easier to imagine that the tool is moving, it is necessary to redefine some movements. On a vertical machining centre, for example, in order to achieve a tool movement in relation to the workpiece in the X positive or plus direction it is necessary to program a machine slide movement in the X negative or minus direction.

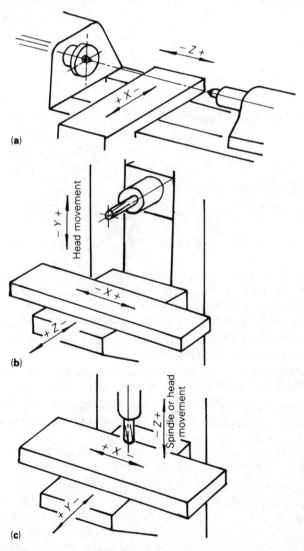

Figure 1.6 *Identification of slides and direction of the slide movement on common machine tools* **(a)** *centre lathe (turning centre)* **(b)** *horizontal milling machine (horizontal machining centre)* **(c)** *vertical milling machine (vertical machining centre).*

In addition to linear movement, the production of a part may also require rotary movement which is provided by the use of ancillary equipment such as rotary tables and indexers. These movements are also controlled via the machining program and are identified by the letters A, B and C as illustrated in Figure 1.7.

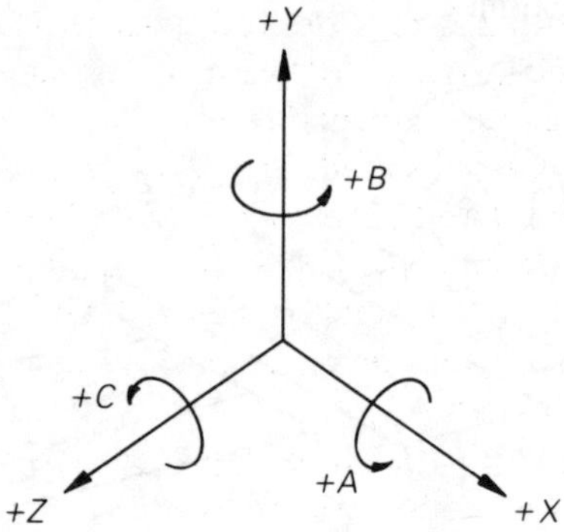

Figure 1.7 *Identification of rotary movements.*

Datums

There are two datums involved in CNC machining that concern the part progammer.

The first of these is the program datum which is established by the programmer when writing the program. This datum is at the intersection of the X, Y and Z axes when milling, and at the intersection of the X and Z axes when turning. In both cases it is given the numerical identity of zero. The actual position of this datum in relation to the workpiece is optional, although there are certain factors to be taken into consideration.

The program datum is, in effect, the point of departure from which the initial slide movements in each axis will be made, and these movements will be dimensionally related to this datum. When program data are stated in absolute terms (see below) all subsequent moves will also be dimensionally related to that point.

The second datum that concerns the part programmer is the machine datum. This datum is a set position for the machine slides where the axes intersect, and it has a numerical identity of zero within the control system.

On some machines the machine datum is a permanently established position and cannot be altered, although it can be repositioned on a temporary basis via a zero 'shift' or 'offset' facility. On other machines a new datum can be established anywhere within the operating pocket of the machine, a facility referred to as a 'floating zero'.

Clearly, there must be some correlation between the machine datum and the program datum when setting the machine if the programmed slide movements are to achieve the intended effect, and the practicalities involved are discussed in more detail in Chapter 2.

Absolute and incremental positional data

Once the direction of movement has been established the distance moved by the machine slide to bring it to a desired position has to be dimensionally defined. This is achieved by the use of linear co-ordinates, with the dimensions being stated in absolute or incremental terms.

A third method is sometimes used, involving the use of polar co-ordinates. This requires a distance stated in relation to a defined point and at an angle stated in relation to a datum axis. It generally requires the control system to include a special programming facility as described on page 28.

Absolute dimensional definition requires all slide movements to be related to a pre-determined zero datum.

Incremental dimensional definition requires each slide movement to be related to the final position of the previous move.

Figure 1.8(a) shows the details of a turned component. The intersection of the spindle centre line and the face of the work is the program zero datum. Assume that a final trace of the component profile is to be programmed.

The dimensional definition in absolute and incremental values that would be required to define slide movement is shown in Figures 1.8(b) and 1.8(c) respectively.

In Figure 1.9(a) the details of a milled component are given. Absolute and incremental dimensional values required to program the machining of the slot are shown in Figures 1.9(b) and 1.9(c) respectively.

Earlier programming languages required dimensional data to be stated in *either* absolute or incremental terms. Modern controllers often provide a 'mix and match' facility that permits the use of both within the same program, and even within the same data block. The distinction is achieved by the continued use of X, Y and Z for absolute values and U, V and W for incremental values.

Circular interpolation

It was explained earlier in the text that circular arc programming on conversational MDI systems has been reduced to a simple data entry that specifies the target position, the value of the radius and the direction of rotation. This simple method of defining circular movement, but with the direction of rotation being defined by the appropriate G code, is available on some word address systems (see page 86) but many systems employ one of two slightly more complex techniques.

Common to all programming systems is the need to determine whether the relative tool travel to produce a particular arc is in a clockwise (CW) or counter-clockwise (CCW) direction. The following approach is usually helpful:

1. For milling operations look along the machine spindle towards the surface being machined.
2. For turning operations look down onto the top face of the cutting tool. (For inverted tooling this involves looking up at the tool from below.)

It should be noted that this technique does not always correspond with the definition adopted by the control systems manufacturers. A simple trial program entered into the machine will clarify the situation.

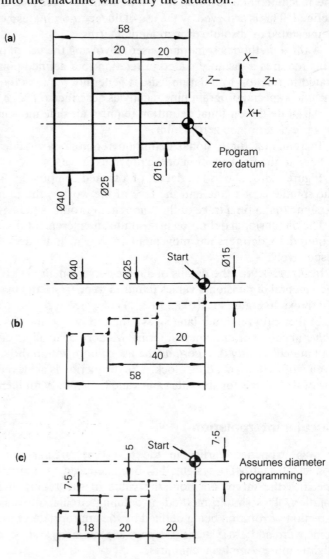

Figure 1.8 (a) *component detail* (b) *absolute dimensions* (c) *incremental dimensions*.

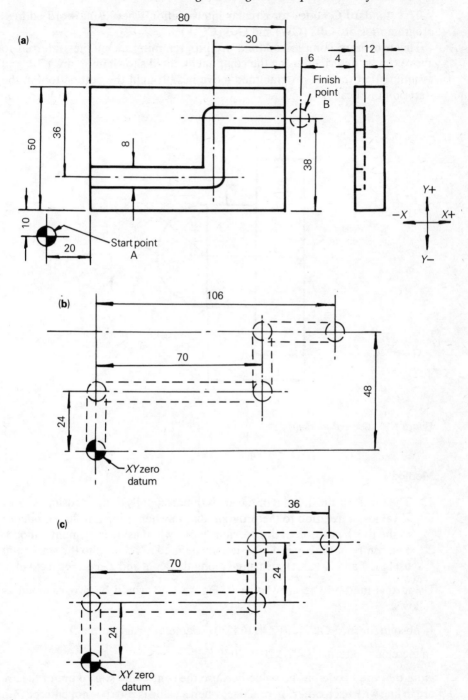

Figure 1.9 **(a)** *component detail* **(b)** *absolute dimensions* **(c)** *incremental dimensions*

The standard G codes for circular interpolation when using word address programming are G02 (CW) and G03 (CCW).

The two more complex address arc programming techniques referred to above can be described using the component detail shown in Figure 1.10, and assuming that the last programmed move has brought the cutting tool to the start point indicated.

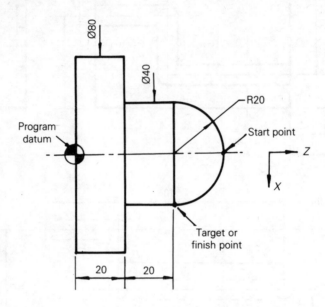

Figure 1.10 *Component detail.*

Method 1

1. The target or finish point of the arc is dimensionally defined, using X, Y or Z values, in relation to the program datum when using absolute mode, or to the finish position of the previous move when using incremental mode.
2. The centre of the arc is dimensionally defined in relation to the start point using I, J and K values measured along the X, Y and Z axes respectively.

Using this method the arc shown in Figure 1.10 would be programmed as follows:

In absolute terms: G02 X40 Z40 I0 K20 (Diameter programming)

In incremental terms: G02 X20 Z-20 I0 K20

Note that the I code has no value because the centre and start point of the arc are in line with each other. In practice, when a value is zero it is not entered into the program. In this method of arc definition the I, J and K values are unsigned.

Method 2

The second method of word address arc programming differs in the way the arc centre is defined. The following data are required:

1. The target or finish point of the arc is dimensionally defined, using X, Y and Z values, in relation to the program datum when using absolute mode, or to the finish position of the previous move when using incremental mode.
2. The centre of the arc is dimensionally defined in relation to the program datum using I, J and K values measured along the corresponding X, Y and Z axes respectively.

Using this second method of programming the arc shown in Figure 1.11 would be programmed as follows:

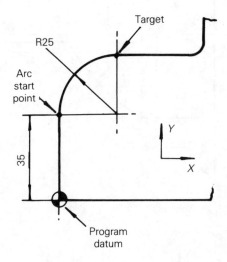

Figure 1.11 *Milled component detail.*

In absolute terms: G02 X25 Y60 I25 J35

In incremental terms: G02 X25 Y25 I25 J35

It is possible when using this approach for the I, J and K values to be negative, as illustrated in Figure 1.12. These values are, therefore, signed plus or minus.

The two arc programming methods described will cater for movement within one quadrant only with each block of program data. Thus programming a complete circular move would require four blocks of data. Similarly, blending arcs would require a separate block of data for each quadrant involved. This latter situation is illustrated in Figure 1.13; the first block would take the tool from point A to point B, and the second block would continue the movement from point B to point C.

When the start and/or stop points do not coincide with an X, Y or Z axis, that is the arc is not exactly 90° or a multiple of 90°, it will be necessary to make a series of calculations.

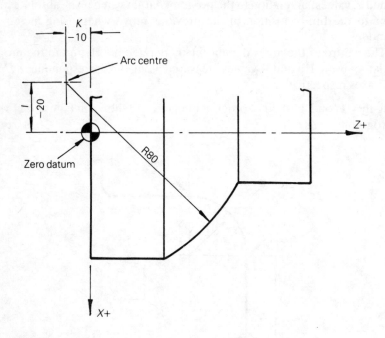

Figure 1.12 *Circular interpolation: negative I and K values.*

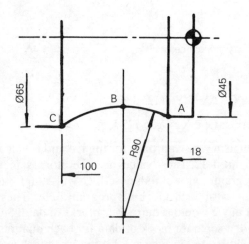

Figure 1.13 *Profile detail requiring two arcs to be programmed.*

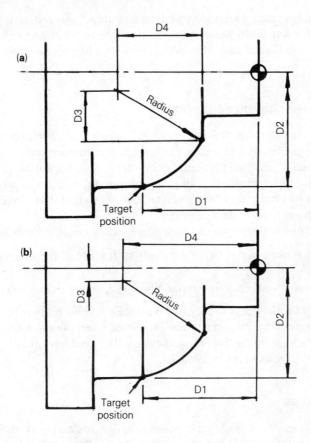

Figure 1.14 *Calculations for arcs less than 90° **(a)** method 1 **(b)** method 2.*

Consider the part detail shown in Figure 1.14(a) and again in Figure 1.14(b), each diagram relating to an arc programming method as indicated. Whichever of the two methods is used, the target position indicated by the dimensions D1 and D2 will have to be dimensionally defined. It will also be necessary to calculate the additional dimensions indicated on each drawing as D3 and D4, these latter dimensions being expressed in the part program as I and K values. There are a number of calculation problems of this type included in Chapter 4.

To conclude these notes on circular interpolation, mention should be made of multi-quadrant programming. This facility is now available on many control systems currently in use. As the description suggests, arcs spanning more than one quadrant can be programmed using just one block of program data.

Toleranced dimensions

It is often the case that dimensions on drawings are toleranced, thus permitting a higher and lower limit. Since it is only possible to enter one value into the control unit it is logical that this should be the middle value of the tolerance band.

Repetitive machining sequences

There are a number of repetitive sequences which are commonly used when machining a variety of components. Other less common sequences are also repetitive, but on only one particular component. It is helpful, since it reduces the program length and also simplifies programming, if such a sequence can be programmed just once; it is then given an identity so that it can be called back into the program as and when required.

Repetitive machining sequences can be generally classified as follows:

(a) Canned or fixed cycles that are an inbuilt feature of the machine control system.
(b) User or programmer defined routines to suit the particular job in hand.

The facility for the programmer to devise special routines may be restricted, especially on small training machines. However, even the most simple system will usually include one or two canned cycles. The controls fitted to advanced machines will have as many as 19 or 20.

Canned cycles

In a text of this nature it would be impossible to deal in detail with all the canned cycles that are available, but the review that follows will convey a good impression of the range currently in use and likely to be encountered. More specifically, the student is advised to make a careful study of the programming methods and techniques associated with the control system he or she will be using. In this respect a close examination of the examples found in the programming manuals will be found to be helpful. The point to remember is that the use of canned cycles is an aid to programming efficiency and accuracy, and they should be used whenever possible.

Perhaps the most widely used machining sequence is that of drilling a hole, and there are few controls that fail to cater for this requirement by including a canned cycle. Indeed, with word address programming, early attempts were made to standardise a drill cycle. That this was quite successful is evident by the fact that the use of G81 for the purpose is as common as the use of G00 and G01 for linear movement control and G02 and G03 for circular interpolation.

There are a number of machining variations necessary in the production of drilled holes.

One of the most commonly used is the basic drilling movement, catered for by the drilling cycle illustrated in Figure 1.15. This involves a drill movement to the required depth at a controlled feed rate, followed by rapid withdrawal.

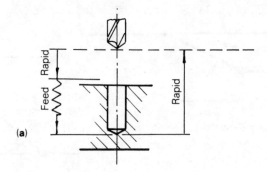

Figure 1.15 *Drill cycle.*

Also widely used is the intermittent or 'peck' drill cycle for deep holes illustrated in Figure 1.16. This illustration shows a complete withdrawal to the Z axis clearance plane after each peck, but variations of this cycle provide for a smaller withdrawal that conveniently breaks the chip but does not give total chip clearance.

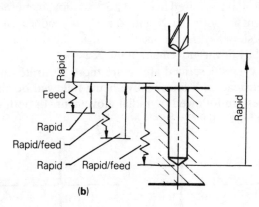

Figure 1.16 *Peck drill cycle.*

A further refinement of this cycle provides for automatic variation of the peck length as the hole deepens. This is achieved by including a 'multiplier' in the cycle data. For example, a multiplier of 0.8 will have the effect of reducing each peck length to 0.8 of the previous peck. To avoid the reduction continuing *ad infinitum* a minimum peck length is also programmed.

Closely allied to the drilling cycles are those for counterboring and tapping. To ensure a clean surface, counterboring requires the inclusion of a time dwell at the extent of cutter travel. Tapping requires that the direction of spindle rotation is reversed to allow withdrawal of the tap.

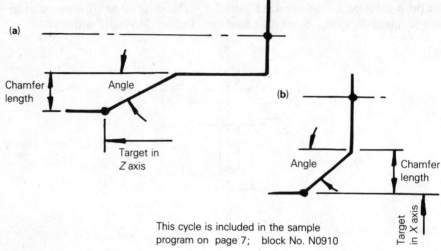

Figure 1.17 *Chamfering cycles.*

Many turning operations involve machining the features catered for by the cycles illustrated in Figures 1.17a and 1.17b. It is possible to program a cycle that would normally require two data blocks in just one block. Figure 1.17a shows the programming data required to effect a Z axis movement followed by simultaneous movement in both the X and Z axes to produce an angle or chamfer. Figure 17.b shows a similar facility, but in this case the angular movement is preceded by linear movement in the X axis.

Very similar to the cycles described above are those illustrated in Figures 1.18(a) and 1.18(b). Instead of a linear move being followed by an angular move, the linear moves are followed by radial movement. In both cases the radial movement must be a full 90°.

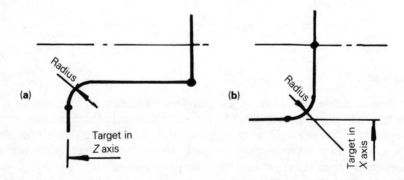

This cycle is included in the sample program on page 7; block No. N0900

Figure 1.18 *90° arc cycles*

Figure 1.19 illustrates a slightly more complex cycle. In this case it is possible to program a linear move either parallel or at an angle to the X axis followed by a blending radius which then leads into an angular move. A final blending radius is optional. This particular cycle reduces four lines of program data to just one. At the same time it completely eliminates the fairly complicated calculation needed to determine profile intersection points—the points at which the first linear move ends and the radial move starts, and where the radial move ends and the second linear move begins.

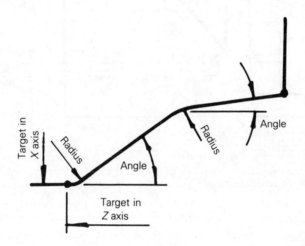

Figure 1.19 *Combined linear moves with arcs cycle.*

Figure 1.20 shows a very useful stock removal cycle. From one data block, plus blocks defining the component profile, the controller will automatically determine the number of passes necessary to remove the excess material, constantly varying the length of travel in the Z axis if need be, and finally taking a finishing cut to reduce the component profile precisely to size. The definition of the component profile in program data is added at the end of the program, and automatically activated via the stock removal cycle call. The profile definition can be achieved by the inclusion of appropriate minor cycles such as those described above.

This stock removal cycle is for application along the Z axis. Similar cycles cater for stock removal along the face of a workpiece.

Figures 1.21 and 1.22 illustrate cycles which may be used for reducing the diameter at any position along the length of a part, and grooving. Figure 1.23 illustrates a screw-cutting cycle, an essential feature of any control system devoted to turning. This particular version of a screw-cutting cycle is particularly easy to use. From just one block of data the control automatically determines the number of passes necessary to achieve the required thread depth. In the block of data shown G84 is the cycle code, X specifies the thread root diameter, Z specifies the thread length, the P_1 value is the depth of the first

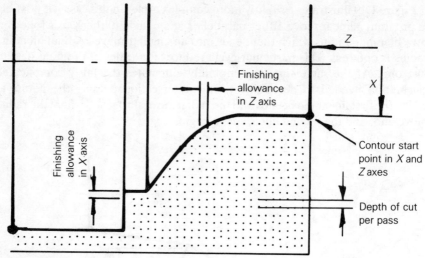

Further data required:

(1) Profile data (added at end of program);

(2) Profile data start block number;

(3) Profile data end block number.

A final profile trace is optional.

This cycle is included in the sample program on page 6 ; block No. N0350

Figure 1.20 *Stock removal to a defined contour cycle.*

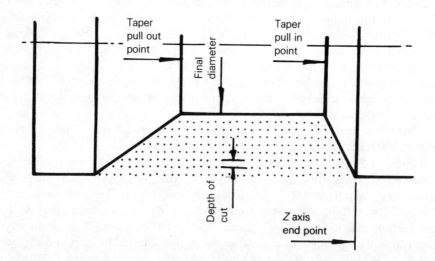

Figure 1.21 *Stock removal cycle with optional tapered entry and exit.*

pass and P_2 is the lead. The control automatically effects a progressive reduction in the depth of cut of each pass that results in improved surface finish and prolonged tool life.

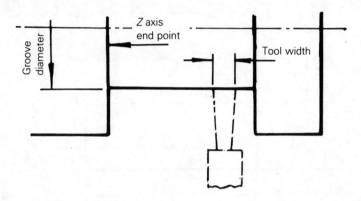

Figure 1.22 *Stock removal or grooving cycle.*

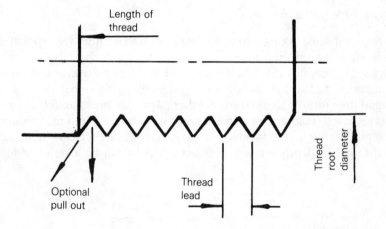

Data example: G84X8.168Z-20P$_1$ I P$_2$ I.5

Figure 1.23 *Automatic threading cycle.*

On less sophisticated screw-cutting cycles the X diameter for each pass along the thread length has to be predetermined by the part programmer, and each pass is programmed in a separate data block.

The range of canned cycles used in milling machine control systems is equally helpful to the part programmer.

Fairly common is the provision of a face milling cycle such as that illustrated in Figure 1.24, where a data input specifies the dimensions of the face to be milled. From this information the control unit will determine the number of

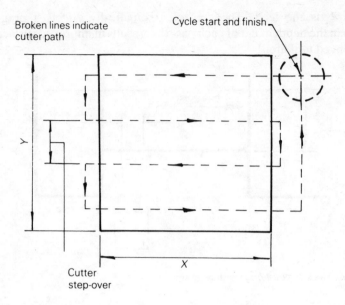

Figure 1.24 *Face milling cycle.*

passes required while taking into consideration a stated cutter overlap that will ensure the face is evenly machined.

Figure 1.25 illustrates a slot milling cycle. Here again the overall dimensions are programmed. The first pass made by the cutting tool goes through the centre and then returns to the start. Further passes are made until the correct depth is achieved, the number of passes necessary being determined from the programmed movement to be made in the Z axis before each cut commences. When the correct depth is reached the cutter path will be a series of loops

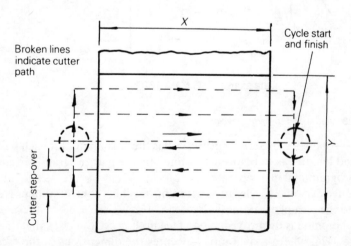

Figure 1.25 *Slotting cycle.*

increasing in size with each pass. As with the face milling cycle, the control unit will determine the number of loops necessary to machine the slot to size, again taking into consideration the need for each cutter pass to overlap to provide a completely clean surface.

Similar to the slot milling cycle is the pocket milling cycle. This cycle commences at the centre of the pocket, the cutter feeding in the Z axis to a programmed depth. There follows a series of loops until the programmed X and Y dimensions are reached, again with a cutter overlap on each pass. If the pocket depth is such that more than one increment in the Z axis is necessary, the cutter is returned to the centre of the pocket and the cycle is repeated. Some systems provide for a cycle that roughs out the main pocket and then machines it to size with a small finishing cut. A pocket milling cycle is illustrated in Figure 1.26.

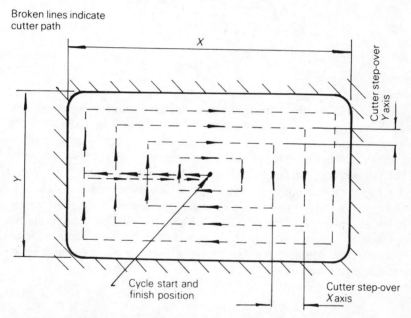

Figure 1.26 *Pocket milling cycle.*

Figure 1.27 shows another widely used cycle referred to as a 'bolt hole circle'. This is for drilling a series of equally spaced holes on a pitch circle diameter. Given that the cutter has been brought to the pole position indicated, the other dimensional data required are the position of the first hole, the Z axis movement, the pitch diameter or radius depending upon the control system, and the number of holes required. The control will make all the necessary calculations to convert the polar co-ordinates to linear co-ordinates and will effect side movements accordingly.

A variation of this cycle will cater for just two or three holes positioned in an angular relationship to each other. An example is detailed in Figure 1.28.

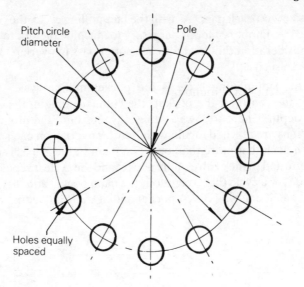

Figure 1.27 *Bolt hole circle.*

Again, the pole position is programmed and the cutter will be in this position when the cycle commences. The additional data that will be required are the Z axis movement, the polar radius and the polar angle(s); the controller will convert this information to slide movement in the relative axes.

Further milling cycles include those for boring, threading, elliptical profiles and even for the machining of helical arcs which simply requires data defining an arc in the X and Y axes and the change in the Z axis dimension between the start and end point. A moment's thought about the mathematical complexity of programming a cutter path such as this should be more than sufficient to emphasise how valuable canned cycles are as an aid to simplifying part programming procedures.

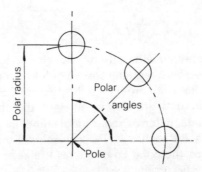

Figure 1.28 *Positioning using polar co-ordinates.*

User defined routines

Canned cycles cater for the easy programming of machined features that are often required on a wide range of components. But the part programmer is often confronted with a feature which is repeated a number of times on a particular component but is found only on that component or a limited range of components. It is in situations such as this that the facility to devise a special routine for use as and when required is very helpful.

Consider the component detail shown in Figure 1.29. Along the length of the shaft is a series of identical recesses. If there is no facility to write a special program, or routine, to machine these recesses the programmer is faced with the rather cumbersome task of detailing each move necessary to machine one recess and then repeating the data for each of the others.

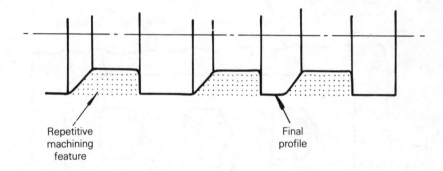

Figure 1.29 *Application of a turning sub-routine.*

When preparing a routine to accomplish a specific machining task such as this the programmer can include any of the available canned cycles that might be appropriate. For example, the profile of the shaft recess referred to could be machined using the cycle illustrated in Figure 1.19, which permitted one-block programming of a linear move in the Z axis followed by an angular move with a blending radius between the two. When specific routines are programmed within other routines they are said to be 'nested'.

Assume the component shown in Figure 1.30 has a repetitive feature as indicated that justifies using a specially devised routine to clear the recess and mill it to the required profile. Now assume that within each of these recesses there is a series of three smaller recesses as shown in Figure 1.31. Since there will be three times as many smaller recesses as larger recesses, a further specially devised routine to machine them will be justified.

The routine for machining the larger recess will therefore contain the sub-routine for machining the smaller recess. The sub-routine is nested within the first routine and will be activated three times during the machining of the larger recess.

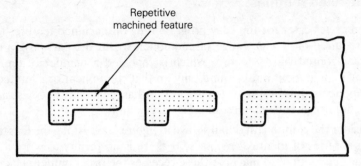

Figure 1.30 *Component detail: application of a milling sub-routine.*

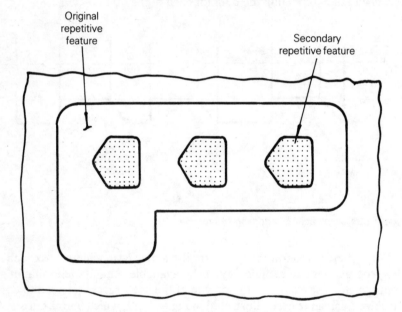

Figure 1.31 *Nesting of sub-routines.*

It would be quite feasible for each of the smaller recesses to include a drilled hole, and this could also be produced using a canned cycle. The sub-routine for the smaller recess would now include a nested drilling cycle.

There are usually some limitations regarding nesting. Some controllers permit sub-routines within sub-routines up to eight deep; others may accept only half this number.

Specially devised routines can also be used to control machine movements and functions not directly associated with metal cutting. For example, a special routine can be used to establish and readily recall predetermined parameters relating to machine slide positions and programming modes which may, for safety reasons, need to be established from time to time throughout the program run. The application of a programmer-devised safety routine is included in the sample program listed on pages 5, 6 and 7.

The safety routine in this instance is determined by the blocks N10 to N70. It can be seen that, throughout the program, these data blocks are activated by a G25 program entry. Block N400 is one example where the safety routine is being called. Each time the routine appears in the program the slides return to a safe indexing position and a set of known operating modes are re-established. This provides a basis from which the programmer can proceed with the programming of further machining operations.

Loops

Some control systems provide a 'loop' facility. This enables the programmer to devise a routine and to repeat that routine within the part program a specific number of times. In other words, when the program reaches the end of the routine the control will return, or loop, back to the beginning of the routine again.

Consider the component shown in Figure 1.32 which is to be reduced from 50 mm diameter to 26 mm diameter by a series of cuts each of 2 mm depth.

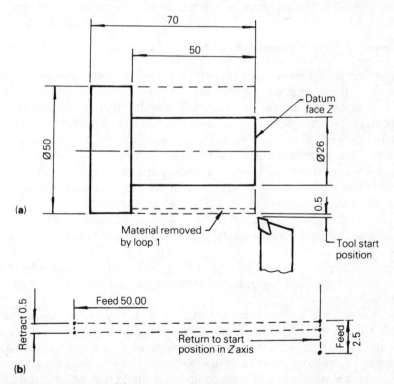

Figure 1.32 *Looping cycle* **(a)** *component detail* **(b)** *loop detail, repeated x 6.*

Assuming the starting point for the tool is as shown, the tool will first move in to a depth of 2.5 mm, thus taking a 2 mm depth of cut, travel along a length of 50 mm, retract 0.5 mm and return to the Z datum, so completing a loop. It will then move in a distance of 2.5 mm, feed along 50 mm, retract 0.5 mm and return to the Z datum, and so on. The loop, including the feed rate, is programmed just once, but is repeated via the loop count data included in the main program as many times as necessary to reduce the work to the required diameter.

Macros

A somewhat specialised type of programmer-devised routine is referred to as a 'macro'. This facility can be used for machining a complete component or a feature of a component that, while not standard in the wider sense, is nevertheless frequently required. For instance, it may commonly occur within the production schedule of a particular company. The macro is given an identity and stored within a separate macro file, or memory, and is called into use as and when required, possibly as an element within a much larger machining program.

A macro may have fixed dimensions, or it may have parametric variables which enable the dimensions to be varied to produce different versions of a basic component. This technique is referred to as 'parametric programming'.

Parametric programming

A parameter is a quantity which is constant in one particular case but variable in others. A simple engineering example of a parameter is the length of a bolt. One version of the bolt will have a certain length; all other versions will be identical, that is, they will have the same thread form, diameter and hexagon head, but they will all vary in length. Thus the length of the bolt is a parameter, constant in one particular case but variable in others.

Parametric programming involves defining parameters and then using those parameters as the basis for one part program that may be used to machine not only the original component but a number of variations as well.

Figure 1.33(a) shows a component the dimensional features of which have been defined as parameters using the symbol # and a number: #1, #2, #3 and so on.

Figures 1.33(b) and 1.33(g) show six variations of the component, the variations being indicated. A range of components such as this is referred to as a family of parts.

The machine movements necessary to machine each of the variations are all included in the original component. Some components require exactly the same movements, but with varying lengths of travel. Other components do not require all of the movements to be made. Using the more usual programming techniques, the production of each component would require a separate part

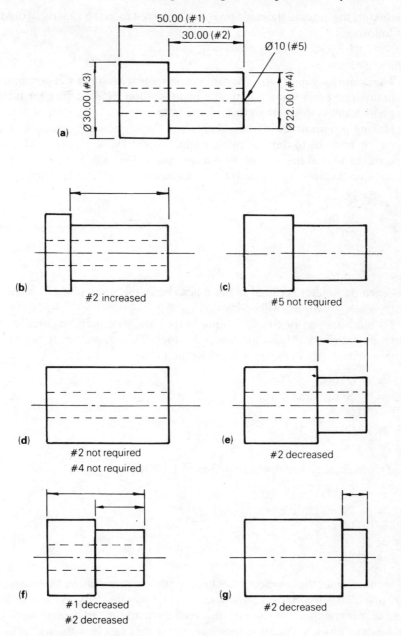

Figure 1.33 *Parametric programming: a family of parts.*

program. Using the parametric part programming technique, instead of defining each dimensional movement individually in the X and Z axes, the parametric reference is programmed. Thus, to turn along the stepped diameter, the entry in the main program, referred to as the 'macro', would read as follows:

N07   G01   *X#4*
NO8 *Z#2*

These entries would suffice for all components requiring a stepped diameter. Equally, one entry using parametric identification would suffice for facing all the components to length or drilling the hole.

Having programmed all movements and the sequence in which they are to occur, it remains to dimensionally define them. The dimensional details are entered as a list at the start of the part program. Thus the parameters and their dimensional values for the original components would read as follows:

#1 = − 50.00
#2 = − 30.00
#3 = 30.00
#4 = 22.00
#5 = 10.00

As each parameter is called in the macro body the programmed dimensional entry made previously will be invoked.

To machine any of the variations in the family of parts requires a simple amendment of the original parametric values. The parameters to machine the component shown in Figure 1.33(b) would be:

#1 = − 50.00
#2 = − 40.00 (amended)
#3 = 30.00
#4 = 22.00
#5 = 10.00

and to machine the component in Figure 1.33(f):

#1 = − 40.00 (amended)
#2 = − 20.00 (amended)
#3 = 30.00
#4 = 22.00
#5 = 10.00

Now consider the components where the programmed movements necessary for machining the basic component are not required. By using a relatively simple programming technique the control unit can be caused to skip the redundant blocks. The necessary program entry involves the use of certain conditional expressions in which assigned abbreviations are used, such as the following:

EQ = equal to
NE = not equal to
GT = greater than

LT = less than
GE = greater than or equal to
LE = less than or equal to

Consider Figure 1.33(d) and assume the #1 and #3 have been machined. In the macro body the next call will be to machine the stepped diameter. To avoid this, blocks must be slipped and so an entry in the macro body will read as follows:

N15 IF [#4 EQ 0] GO TO N18

This statement says that if #4 is zero, move on to block number 18. Since #4 is non-existent in the component, the parametric value will be entered as zero and consequently the control unit will move ahead.

The above description of the use of the parametric programming technique is a very simple one. It is in fact a very powerful concept and its full application quite complex. For instance, parameters may be mathematically related within the macro body, that is, they may be added together, subtracted from one another, and so on.

In addition, the parametric principle may be extended to include speed and feeds, when all the likely variations for roughing, finishing, etc. may be given a parametric identity and called into the program as and when required.

Point definition

Point definition is a programming facility, not widely available, which simplifies programming for drilling operations. With this facility it is possible to dimensionally define as many as 99 points or positions, and enter them into a special file within the control memory. The file can be accessed as required, the points positions appearing in tabular form.

The points required for inclusion are entered at the start of a part program, and might look as follows:

N1	G78	P1	X15	Y20
N2	G78	P2	X20	Y20
N3	G78	P3	X50	Y30
N4	G78	P4	X65	Y60
N5	G78	P5	X75	Y75
N6	G78	P6	X98	Y78

To drill a hole to a specified depth of 20 mm, using a G81 drilling cycle at points 2, 5 and 6, would require a program entry as follows:

| N095 | G81 | Z-20 | F150 | S1850 |
| N100 | G79 | P2 | P5 | P6 |

The more holes to be drilled, the more advantageous the use of the facility becomes. The dimensional date relating to each point can be modified to suit any particular job.

Mirror image

Mirror image is the term used to describe a programming facility used to machine components, or features of components, that are dimensionally identical but geometrically opposite either in two axes or one axis. By using the mirror image facility such components can be machined from just one set of data.

In Figure 1.34 an original component feature is indicated in the bottom left-hand corner of the diagram. A complete mirror image of that feature is shown in the top right-hand corner, while mirror images in the X axis and the Y axis are shown respectively in the bottom right and top left-hand corners of the diagram.

To produce a complete mirror image both the X axis and Y axis dimensional values will change from negative to positive. For half mirror images the dimensional values will change from negative to positive in one axis only.

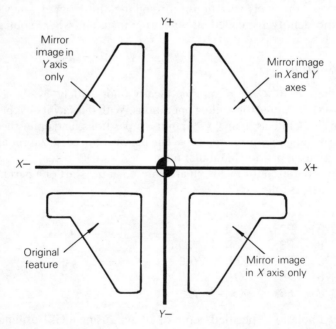

Figure 1.34 *Mirror image.*

Rotation and translation

The position of holes in angular relationship to each other was discussed on page 28. The machined feature—the hole—is rotated about a polar position.

The ability to rotate the position of holes in this way is generally associated with the bolt hole circle facility and is commonly available. Many control systems also have the ability to rotate more complex features. The principle of rotation is illustrated in Figure 1.35.

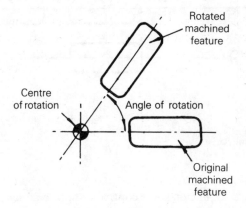

Figure 1.35 *Rotation of machined feature.*

A programming facility closely allied to rotation is translation. This permits the programmer to reposition a feature about a defined pole or centre and then to rotate the feature about a predetermined point on the feature itself. The principle is illustrated in Figure 1.36.

A bonus of the translation facility is that features of complex shape that are required in an angular location, which thus present some fairly complex programming calculations, can be programmed as though they lay on a true XY axis, simplifying the calculations required. They can then be repositioned using translation.

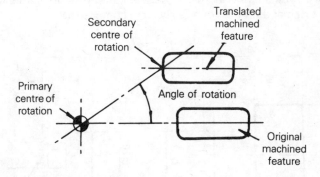

Figure 1.36 *Polar translation.*

Translation may also be defined in linear terms and is, in effect, a datum shift facility. The shift may be in the X or Y axis or in both. Translation defined in this manner is illustrated in Figure 1.37.

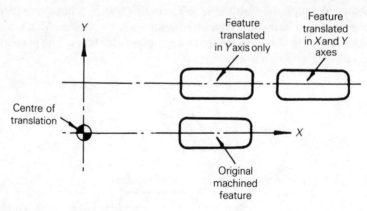

Figure 1.37 *Linear translation.*

Scaling

The scaling facility available on some control systems enables components that are geometrically identical but uniformly variable dimensionally to be produced from the same program data.

Figure 1.38 illustrates two components, the production of which could be accommodated by scaling. Scaling is also available for milling operations. It can be applied to complete components or to one feature of a component.

An example of a scaling factor range, available on a widely-used vertical machining centre, is from 0.002 to 250. With such an extensive range the desired reduction or increase in size could well involve a machining requirement outside the capabilities of the machine, in which case an error message would be indicated. In practice components likely to be considered for production by scaling would rarely involve the use of widely varying scaling factors, but even a small scale factor, say 2, could produce an unacceptable result if the original data was for a fairly large component.

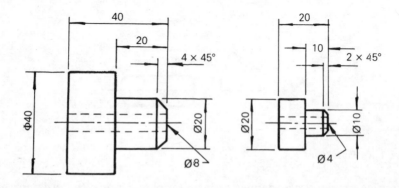

Figure 1.38 *Geometrically identical components suitable for production by scaling.*

It is possible to use the lower end of a scaling factor range to minutely increase or decrease the machined size in one or more axes to maintain a dimensional tolerance that may be being lost owing, for example, to the effect of clamping or distortion of the workpiece.

Block delete

Production engineering often involves machining a range of components that have slight variations from each other. For example, a hole which has to be drilled in one component is not required in a second component, although all the other details remain the same. Thus one program would serve for both components providing that some means exists for not drilling the hole when it is not required. The way this is achieved is by use of a 'block delete' facility.

Blocks relating to machining features which may not always be required incorporate the symbol / which is referred to as a slash. The exact position of the slash within the block may vary from one system to another, but it is usually at the start.

The machine operator will need to be instructed as to whether the data is to be retained or deleted from the current machining task. If the data is to be ratained the operator takes no action. If the data is to be deleted the operator has to activate the block delete button on the control panel before running the program. Activation of the button is usually indicated by a light.

If the slash delete button is not activated the control will respond to all the data contained in the program. If the slash delete button is activated then all the blocks containing a slash will be ignored.

On some control systems if the slash delete button is not activated the program will automatically stop when the first slash is reached and the operator then has to make a positive response, either to activate the data contained within the slashes or delete them.

The block delete facility is also useful when machining castings or forgings, where stock removal requirements may vary. The operator is given the option to include an extra cut or not as necessary.

The use of the block delete facility relies on a clear and concise relay of instructions between the part programmer and the machine operator. The machine operator must be left in no doubt as to what is required.

Program stops

Apart from the program stop that is automatically effected when the end of a program is reached, and which arrests all slide and spindle motion, there are two other situations where a halt in proceedings may need to be included in the part program.

The first of these is the point at which the operator is required to carry out some specific task directly associated with the machining program, such as resetting the work or replacing a tool. With word address programming this is normally achieved by programming M00. When such a stop is effected it is essential that the operator knows exactly what has to be done before the program is reactivated.

The second type of program stop is used when a halt in activity is not quite so critical, and the operator decides whether a stop is actually made. This type of stop is referred to as 'optional' and will only take place if the operator has activated the optional stop button on the control console. The programmer may include an optional stop in the program whenever he or she considers it may be of value to the machine operator, such as when a dimensional check or an inspection of the tooling condition is appropriate. But quite often it is the operator who will edit into the program, via the control console, stops that will permit the solving of particular problems that have presented themselves during the machining process. The optional stop in a word address program is normally effected via a programmed M01.

In addition to the stops included in the part program the operator has, of course, recourse to an emergency stop should the need arise.

Questions

1 Devise a simple diagram to illustrate the axes of movement of a vertical machining centre and explain why it is necessary to redefine some of these movements as an aid to part programming.

2 Make a simple sketch to show the difference between absolute and incremental dimensional data.

3 How is the difference between an incremental and absolute value indicated on word address control systems that permit the use of either in the same part program?

4 What value should be programmed when a drawing states an upper and lower limit to a toleranced dimension?

5 Briefly explain the difference in data required by the two methods of circular interpolation which use I, J and K values.

6 Explain when the use of a programmer-devised sub-routine would be justified.

7 How does a 'macro' differ from other types of programmer-devised routines?

8 Describe the concept of 'parametric' programming and suggest when its use would be advantageous.

9 Describe the programming technique of 'point definition' and describe the type of situation where it could be used to advantage.

10 With the aid of simple sketches explain the difference between the programming facilities referred to as 'translation' and 'rotation'.

2

MANUAL PART PROGRAMMING

Definition

Manual part programming is the term used to describe the preparation of a part program without recourse to computing facilities to determine cutter paths, profile intersecting points, speeds and feeds etc.

Procedure

Taking as a starting point the detail drawing of the component to be manufactured, the tasks which confront the part programmer may be listed as follows:

1. Select a machine capable of handling the required work.
2. Prepare a schedule of machining operations.
3. Determine work holding and location techniques.
4. Determine tooling requirements and their identity.
5. Document, or otherwise record, instructions relating to work holding, work location and tooling.
6. Calculate suitable cutting speeds and feed rates.
7. Calculate profile intersecting points, arc centres etc.
8. Determine appropriate tool paths including the use of canned cycles and sub-routines.
9. Prepare the part program.
10. Prove the part program and edit as necessary.
11. Record the part program for future use.

Although these stages have been given a separate identity they are very much interrelated and cannot be treated in isolation. A diagrammatic impression of the approach to be adopted is given in Figure 2.1.

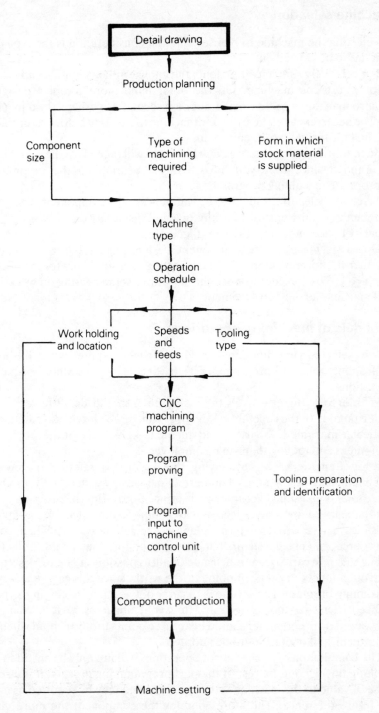

Figure 2.1 *Procedures associated with part programming.*

Machine selection

In selecting the machine to be used the first consideration is the type of work that has to be carried out.

For relatively simple components the choice will be obvious and is likely to involve just one machine. On the other hand more complex designs may require machining to be carried out on a second or perhaps third machine. It may be necessary to move from one machine to a second before returning to the original for further work, and so on.

Such transfers, and the stage at which they will take place, need to be clearly determined since they will have a direct bearing on the preparation of appropriate machining programs.

Machine selection will also be influenced by component size and the programmer must ensure that any machine used has the necessary physical capacity to accommodate the workpiece.

Decisions made at the component design stage relating to materials— whether the form of supply will be a casting or a solid bar, for instance—will also need to be considered since this may have some bearing on work-holding and machine-loading arrangements.

Schedule of machining operations

Having selected a machine capable of handling the required work, the next task confronting the part programmer is to decide on a suitable sequence of operations.

In order to do this effectively the programmer should ideally have a thorough understanding of the capabilities and operating procedures associated with the particular machine to be used, and adequate knowledge of the work-holding equipment and tooling that can be employed.

It is often the case that, giving due regard to safety requirements, a machining task can be tackled in more than one way with equally good results in terms of dimensional accuracy and surface finish. But the programmer must always bear in mind one objective is to complete the machining as quickly as possible. There are two basic planning techniques that, when carefully considered, can make a significant contribution to achieving this objective.

The first is to carry out as much machining as possible at one work setting and to avoid unnecessary repositioning of the work, since this can be a very time-consuming business. The second is to carry out as much machining as possible with each cutting tool called, and to avoid unnecessary tool changing or indexing. The programmer should bear these points firmly in mind when listing the sequence of operations to be adopted.

The compilation of a schedule of operations will not only be an aid to logical thinking throughout the rest of the part programming process; it is also likely to be of value to the machine setter/operator and may be required as a record for future reference. The more complex the component the more vital the compilation of a schedule becomes.

It is possible that such an operation schedule will form just part of the general documentation relating to a particular job which will also contain information relating to work-holding, tooling, speeds and feeds. The documentation relating to these aspects of part programming are discussed further below.

Work-holding and location

The part programmer's responsibilities regarding work-holding and location are as follows:

(a) determine the work-holding device or devices to be used;
(b) determine if there will be a need to use supplementary support at any stage during a machining sequence;
(c) determine the means of ensuring accurate location of the workpiece prior to machining;
(d) document all matters relating to work setting that will have a direct effect on the validity of the part program and that will, therefore, be of importance to the machine setter/operator.

Decisions made in relation to these factors are greatly influenced by component shape and size. Components of regular shape are usually accommodated in standard work-holding devices such as chucks, collets and vices. Components of irregular shape often require special work-holding arrangements, and as a result demand extra attention from the programmer. He or she may find it necessary to include special slide movements in the program, solely to avoid collisions between the cutting tools and the clamping.

Similarly, the programmer will need to give special attention to components requiring supplementary support—the use of a centre support or steady, for example—and may well have to include control of these features within the part program.

Multi-component settings will also have a direct effect on the approach adopted when preparing the part program.

A special characteristic of CNC machining involving very high rates of metal removal is that considerable cutting forces may be exerted in a number of directions during the production of a single component, with very rapid change from one direction to another, possibly occurring without the safeguard of manual observation or intervention. This variation in cutting force direction means that the prime objective in work location, that of ensuring that the cutting forces are directed against an immovable feature in the work-holding arrangement, may not always be met when using standard equipment. For example, work held in a conventional machine vice is only positively located when the cutting forces are directed against the vice jaw. If the cutting force changes direction so that it is at 90° to the fixed jaw there will be a frictional hold only, which is not foolproof.

When confronted with the problem of multi-directional cutting forces the programmer should give full consideration to the alternative approaches available. Devices such as the grid plate will provide for positive location in several directions, but it may be necessary to use a specially devised fixture. A number of the project components included in Chapter 6 will require this approach.

It is possible that the work-holding equipment available is very limited in range, such as a machine vice. In this situation the programmer will have to make the best of arrangements such as the frictional hold described above. For example, a reduction in metal removal rates will reduce the cutting forces exerted on the workpiece. Each problem encountered will require individual assessment, and the methods used to overcome the problem should be selected with reference to the high safety standards that are so essential in CNC machining.

Another factor that must be considered is that of geometric tolerances, as listed in Appendix 4. When any of these are encountered on a part drawing the programmer must ensure that the work-holding and location arrangements being used will enable them to be achieved. It is a further area of part programming that requires the programmer to be well versed in the practical side of CNC machining, and to have a full understanding of the capabilities and limitations of the work-holding devices that may be used.

In order that specified geometric requirements are satisfied, it may be necessary to adopt a special approach to work setting, or, as is more likely, work re-setting before carrying out further operations. In such cases it is imperative that the part programmer indicates to the machine setter or operator his reasons for doing so. Such information is included in the general documentation relating to that particular workpiece.

The importance of positive location of the workpiece to absorb the forces exerted by the metal-cutting action has already been stressed. There is, however, another reason why the part programmer is concerned about precise location of the work. He or she will program the slide movements in relation to a datum that will be determined when the part program is prepared, and unless the part to be machined is precisely positioned in relation to that datum the intended machining features will not be achieved. Subsequent parts must also be positioned in exactly the same way to ensure uniformity of the product.

When establishing a program zero datum the programmer will have to take into consideration the reference zero position that is an incorporated feature of the machine control system. The machine zero may or may not be in a fixed position. If it is fixed it may be capable of being shifted on a temporary basis via the part program. It may be capable of being established anywhere within the operating pocket of the machine, or there may be limitations on repositioning. Whatever the circumstances the programmer will need to fully understand them.

Consider first a control system that permits a machine zero to be established anywhere the programmer chooses. In this situation it may be considered that the correct programming approach is to establish a machine zero that will correspond with the chosen program zero. So for a component such as the one illustrated in Figure 2.2 the programmer selects the corner of the workpiece as zero for all programmed moves in the X and Y axes, and a 2 mm clearance between the top of the work and the Z axis zero. To ensure that there is correlation between the two zero positions the following machine setting approach will be necessary.

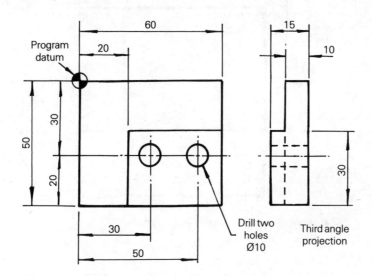

Figure 2.2   *Component detail.*

1. Set the corner of the vice jaw to zero in the X and Y axes (achieved by using a centre locator or 'wobbler', or possibly an electronic probe).
2. Set the Z axis zero 2 mm above the work surface (achieved by touching on to a suitable worksetting block and calibrating the tool length offset accordingly).
3. Locate all workpieces using the corner of the fixed jaw of the vice as a reference position. (A plate attached to the vice jaw may be used to simplify this process).

The setting arrangement that accommodates the X and Y axes requirements is illustrated in Figure 2.3.

Consider now a situation involving a turned component such as that illustrated in Figure 2.4, and assume that the programmer has chosen to establish the face of the part as the Z datum zero and that the machine spindle centre line is the X axis zero, as is normal. All that is required of the programmer is to ensure that the machine setter or operator is aware that the program datum is at the face of the work. The setter or operator will be required to establish the Z axis zero at the machine in the manner appropriate to that particular machine, and then ensure that all workpieces are all set to a measured overhang or to a stop as illustrated in Figure 2.5.

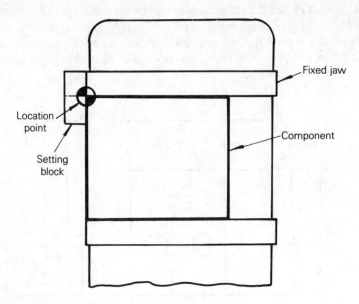

Figure 2.3 *Use of corner fixed jaw for component location.*

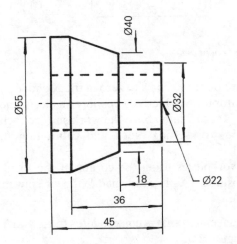

Material: medium carbon steel

Figure 2.4 *Component detail.*

It is often the case that turning centres have a set zero datum for the machine, usually at the back face of the chuck or a reference surface on the spindle nose. This type of zero cannot be changed but can be shifted on a temporary basis.

The programmer may choose to use the back face of the component as the program zero in the Z axis, a technique often applied when work is being

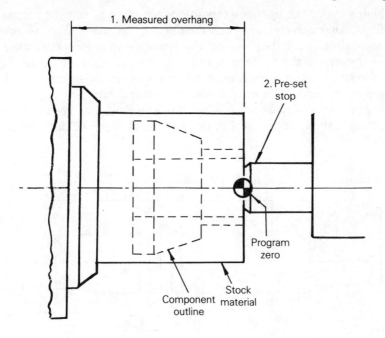

Figure 2.5 *Alternative work setting techniques to establish a datum for turned work.*

produced from prepared billets. Work location is simple, and simply involves ensuring the material is firmly placed against the reference face. A further bonus is that all programmed slide movements will be positive.

To use the facility of repositioning the zero on a temporary basis—so that it corresponds to a program zero established at the workpiece face for instance— it will be necessary for the programmer to determine the amount of shift required to accommodate all the programmed movements in the Z axis. The dimensional value of the shift required, that is, the work overhang, must be documented. Eventually it will be entered manually into the offset file on the control by the machine setter. This offset will be activated via an appropriate program entry such as a G54 or G55.

To ensure that the programmed machine movements achieve the desired effect, the work material has to be accurately positioned, either manually or automatically against stops, and this function is the responsibility of the machine setter or operator. The accuracy of this method of work setting can be improved if the overhang is slightly larger than the actual work requires, allowing a facing cut to be used early in the machining sequence to establish the new zero precisely.

It may be necessary to provide for more than one zero shift within the same turning program. A common situation is when the component length is such that, to ensure adequate support and to avoid chatter, part of the machining is carried out with a reduced overhang. After a programmed stop in the machining cycle, the operator repositions the work to suit the second zero position. Alternatively, the repositioning of the work may be achieved automatically through the program. This is particularly appropriate when a bar feed is concerned, the bar feeding to stops. The provision of a centre support may also be a feature of such an arrangement. After the second zero shift all subsequent moves will be made in relation to that datum.

An example of a component which would involve two zero shifts during machining is shown in Figure 2.6. Because the diameter of the component is

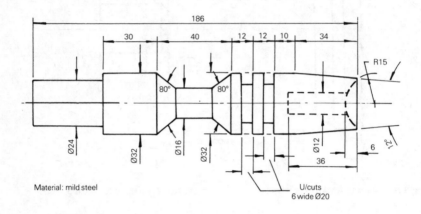

Figure 2.6   *Component detail.*

relatively small in proportion to its length, it would be advisable to use two settings and a centre support for the second sequence of machining operations. The first setting involving the shift of the machine zero to the work face is illustrated in Figure 2.7(a), while the second setting requiring shifting the zero for a second time is shown in Figure 2.7(b).

The use of a second program zero is also applied to milling operations. An initial program zero is established and some machine movements will be made in relation to that datum. Then, via an appropriate program call the zero will be re-established and all subsequent moves will be made in relation to the second datum.

One milling situation where the zero shift facility is particularly useful is when more than one component is to be machined at one setting, as illustrated in Figure 2.8. In this example a grid plate is used as a work-holding device. The advantage of the grid plate is that all the clamping and location points can be identified using a letter/number grid reference, rather iike using a map reference to locate a particular town. Using this reference system the part programmer can instruct the machine setter/operator exactly where to position each component so that their location will correspond with the selected program zeros.

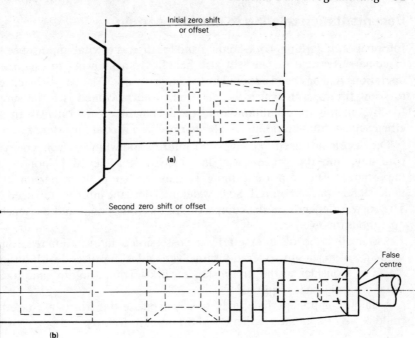

Figure 2.7 *The application of a second zero shift to accommodate work re-setting* **(a)** *first work setting* **(b)** *second work setting.*

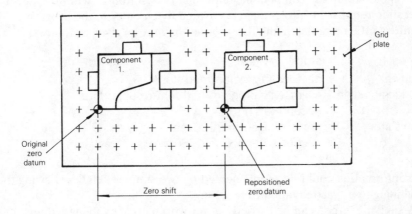

Figure 2.8 *Use of zero shift for multi-component machining at one setting.*

Documentation relating to machine setting

Information regarding work-holding and location is of vital importance to the machine setter. He or she will also benefit from knowing the sequence of operations that has been adopted by the programmer. Also, it will be necessary to know the form in which the material to be machined is to be supplied. Ideally, all this information should be documented, not only as an aid to efficiency on the shop floor, but also to provide a record for future reference.

The documents used to convey this information will vary from company to company, and the precise way in which it is achieved is not of major importance. The important thing is that the shop floor personnel fully understand what is required. So how detailed does the information need to be? The answer depends on the complexity of the component and the machining operations involved.

Assume that the machine setter is in possession of information regarding the sequence of machining operations involved and is to proceed with setting the machine. Consider in the first instance work loading, holding and location. What information is required?

A simple component that is to be turned in one setting from a pre-faced billet could be accommodated with a few short notes as follows:

Material:	prepared billet
Loading:	manual
Work-holding:	chuck
Location:	back face of chuck
Zero shift:	Z-120 mm

The last item would indicate that a manual data entry shifting the Z axis zero from the spindle face to the workpiece face is required.

A more complex component requiring two settings, with the second operation requiring centre support activated by an entry in the program, will require a little more detail and the information may be given as follows:

Material:	stock bar Ø 25
Loading:	bar feed to programmed stops
Working-holding:	collet, with programmed centre support for second setting
Zero shifts:	first setting, G54 Z-100 mm
	second setting, G55 Z-180 mm

This information could be supplemented by two simple sketches showing the machining to be carried out at each setting.

A similar exercise can be carried out for workpieces involving milling. The exercise shown in Figure 2.9 could be produced on a 'one off' basis or involve a multi-component setting.

In the first instance it could be located using the corner of the fixed jaw of the vice as a reference point, a technique referred to on page 47. The instructions necessary to achieve this would be as follows:

Material: prepared blank 80 mm x 40 mm
Work-holding: machine vice
Location: corner of fixed jaw
Program datum: Xaxis -25 mm
                    Yaxis 25 mm
                    Zaxis 2 mm

Again the information regarding the program datum may be more readily understood if the instructions include a sketch.

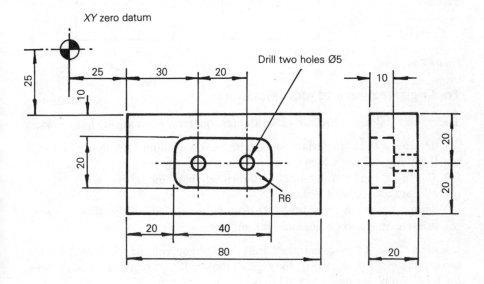

Material: aluminium alloy
Third angle projection

Figure 2.9   *Component detail.*

A multi-component set-up involving the same component could involve the use of a grid plate. To convey the necessary setting information the programmer should be familiar with the grid plate and its associated locating and clamping devices. With such knowledge he may be able to give detailed instructions for the complete setting, using the grid references to position the various setting blocks, locating dowels and clamps to be used in the operation. On the other hand, a competent setter could well manage with the basic information included in Figure 2.10.

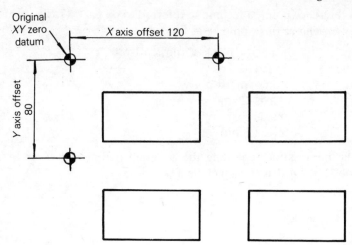

Figure 2.10 *Use of grid plate.*

Tooling selection and identification

The responsibilities of the part programmer concerning tooling are as follows:

(a) determine the appropriate tools to be used, including their shape, size and the material from which they will be made;
(b) allocate identification numbers to facilitate machine setting;
(c) allocate tool offset numbers;
(d) determine, when appropriate, the dimensional value of the offsets;
(e) prepare appropriate documentation.

It is essential that a programmer is fully conversant with the tooling system for the machine involved, that is, the type of tooling that can be used and the way the tools can be located and held in position.

A major feature of CNC machining is the use of standard tooling. The intricate slide movements that are possible greatly minimise the need for special tooling, particularly form tools. In many ways the tooling requirements for CNC machining are less complex than for conventional machining.

Providing the programmer is conversant with the machine tooling system the process of selecting tooling for a particular job is largely a case of selecting and utilising standard items.

It is important that the correct tool material is used, particularly so when using carbide inserts. Reference should be made to manufacturers' literature for guidance in this respect. Appendices 2, 3 and 4 give an indication of the type of information that is available.

It is often the case that the tools available within a company for use on a particular machine will be further standardised with their details being documented. An example of a company-based tool standard is shown in Figure 2.11.

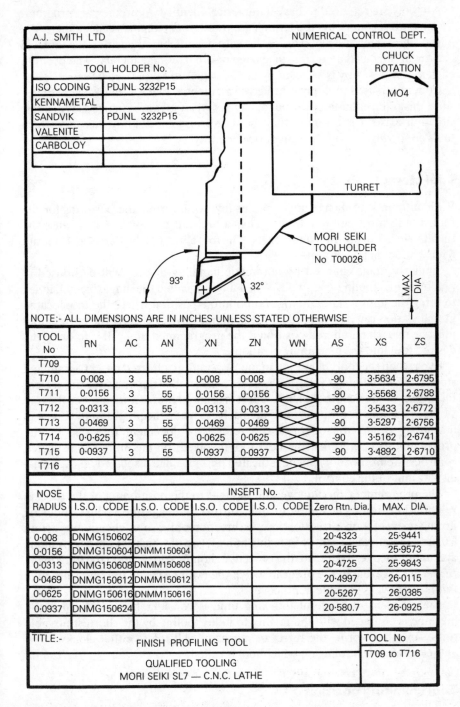

| A.J. SMITH LTD | NUMERICAL CONTROL DEPT. |

TOOL HOLDER No.	
ISO CODING	PDJNL 3232P15
KENNAMETAL	
SANDVIK	PDJNL 3232P15
VALENITE	
CARBOLOY	

CHUCK ROTATION
MO4

TURRET

MORI SEIKI
TOOLHOLDER
No T00026

93°   32°

MAX DIA

NOTE:- ALL DIMENSIONS ARE IN INCHES UNLESS STATED OTHERWISE

TOOL No	RN	AC	AN	XN	ZN	WN	AS	XS	ZS
T709									
T710	0·008	3	55	0·008	0·008		-90	3·5634	2·6795
T711	0·0156	3	55	0·0156	0·0156		-90	3·5568	2·6788
T712	0·0313	3	55	0·0313	0·0313		-90	3·5433	2·6772
T713	0·0469	3	55	0·0469	0·0469		-90	3·5297	2·6756
T714	0·0·625	3	55	0·0625	0·0625		-90	3·5162	2·6741
T715	0·0937	3	55	0·0937	0·0937		-90	3·4892	2·6710
T716									

NOSE RADIUS	INSERT No.				Zero Rtn. Dia.	MAX. DIA.
	I.S.O. CODE	I.S.O. CODE	I.S.O. CODE	I.S.O. CODE		
0·008	DNMG150602				20·4323	25·9441
0·0156	DNMG150604	DNMM150604			20·4455	25·9573
0·0313	DNMG150608	DNMM150608			20·4725	25·9843
0·0469	DNMG150612	DNMM150612			20·4997	26·0115
0·0625	DNMG150616	DNMM150616			20·5267	26·0385
0·0937	DNMG150624				20·580.7	26·0925

TITLE:- FINISH PROFILING TOOL	TOOL No
QUALIFIED TOOLING MORI SEIKI SL7 — C.N.C. LATHE	T709 to T716

Figure 2.11 *Company devised tool standard.*

All tools are required to have a numerical identity within the part program. This identity, commonly the letter T followed by two digits, is allocated by the part programmer and will correspond with the numbered position the tool will occupy in the machine turret, magazine or other storage facility. The position each tool will occupy is affected by factors which are discussed below.

Commonly-used tools are often given an identity that is retained at all times, since this often eliminates the need to re-set when jobs are changed. When this situation exists it is essential that the part programmer knows exactly which tools are involved, and their numerical identity.

Tool storage

With automatic tool changing facilities involving turrets the positions for the tools in the turret are numbered. Thus a tool call of, say, T06 will cause the turret to index to position number six. The tool allocated the numerical identity 6 must be set in position six.

Similarly, tools changed by automatic handling devices will be housed in readiness in a tooling magazine. When a tool is called the magazine will index to bring the appropriate tooling station into a position where the tool located in that station can be accessed by the handling device. Clearly the correct tool must be in each numbered position if the programmed tool call is to bring the desired tool into the machining position.

Even when the tool change is a manual operation, effected by a programmed stop in the machining cycle, the process is assisted if the operator has a clear indication of the next tool to be used. It is usual, therefore, to number the tool storage positions or even the tools themselves. When the programmed break in machining occurs the operator can refer to a document provided by the programmer to determine the next tool involved; on the more sophisticated control systems the tool may be indicated by a message displayed on the visual display unit of the control.

The programmer should give due thought to the positioning of the tools in relationship to each other in the turret or magazine. Most indexing arrangements involve rotation in one direction only, so to change, say, from T03 to T06 will require three indexing moves, two of which are time-consuming and unproductive. Therefore the objective should be to position the tools in the turret or magazine in the order in which they will be called into use, although this is not always possible in practice.

The problem of wasteful indexing time is considerably eased when the machine is equipped with the facility to index tooling by the shortest possible route. In other words, the turret or magazine will rotate either clockwise or anti-clockwise depending on which tool is called.

Tool changing position

The programmer should consider carefully the position the machine slides are to be in when a tool change is made. There is a tendency, particularly among students, to return the machine slides to a set position before making a change, a practice that may have its merits from a safety point of view early in training but which, like wasteful indexing moves, can add considerably to the total time taken to machine the part.

The objective must be to keep non-cutting slide movement to a minimum. For example, on a vertical machining centre it is often possible to effect a tool change immediately above the point at which the tool completes the required machining, the change being carried out after an appropriate Z up-movement of the machine spindle or head. This saves making a long and unnecessary journey to a set position such as the XY zero datum. On turning centres a similar time saving can be achieved by indexing as near to the workpiece as is safely possible.

Tool offsets

Most machining operations involve the use of more than one tool, and usually they vary in length and/or diameter. To accommodate these size variations, and to permit the programmer to assume that all the tools are identical, machine controls are provided with a cutter compensation facility that will, when activated, automatically adjust the programmed slide movements. Thus it enables the programmer to totally ignore tool size and simply program movements that are exactly the same as the profile detail, a technique referred to as 'point' programming.

The task of dealing with variations in tool size is left to the tool setter or operator since it is essentially a case of ascertaining the tool sizes or size variations and entering these numerical values into the machine control.

The numerical values that are required to be entered relate to tool length and tool radius.

The manner in which tool length variations are determined and entered varies with machine type. On some controls they are entered simply as offset values, one tool being used as a reference tool and thus having no offset value, and all other tools having data entries corresponding to their dimensional variation from the reference tool. This principle is illustrated in Figure 2.12.

On other machines the size variations of all tools are determined in relation to a fixed point on the machine, such as the corner of a tool post, as illustrated in Figure 2.13. In this particular example the variations are entered in a tool data file, there being a second file for programmer-devised offsets that are, through appropriate program data, paired with the tool data file entries.

Tool radius and diameter entries are less complex, being simply a case of ascertaining the correct value, by actually measuring the tool if need be, and entering the numerical value as required by the control system of the machine being used.

Since tool data can be entered, modified or erased by the machine operator at will the facility can be used to:

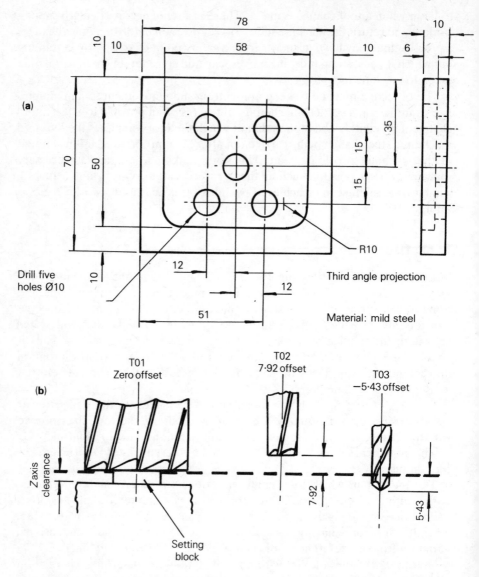

Figure 2.12 *Tool offsets related to a reference tool* **(a)** *component detail* **(b)** *tool offsets.*

(a) accommodate replacement tooling which varies from the original;
(b) make variations to the component size;
(c) initiate a series of cuts, say roughing and finishing, using the same dimensional programmed data.

If the machine operator varies the tool offset values for whatever reason, the effect is temporary. It has no permanent effect on the original program. However, the programmer can utilise the offset facility within the part

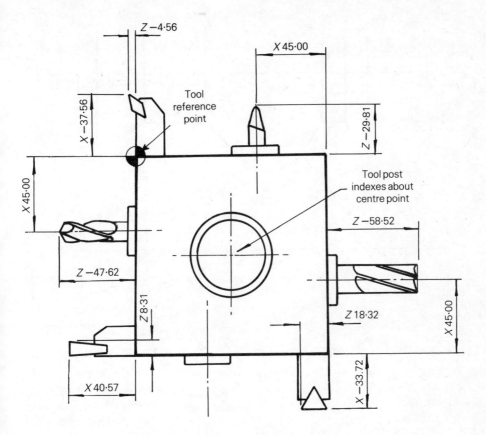

Figure 2.13 *Tool offset data related to a fixed point on the toolpost.*

program, and this creates a situation where accurate communication between the programmer and the shop floor personnel is essential if the programming objectives are to be clearly understood.

Two situations involving tool offsets that are particularly useful from a programming point of view are when variations in the size of components are to be made from the same basic program, and when a series of cuts are to be initiated along a profile using the same programmed dimensional data.

The ability to use offsets in this manner is based on pairing offset values with specific tools. Just as tools are allocated a numerical identity, so are offsets. Two digits are commonly used, just as in the case of tool identity. The offset digits are paired with the tool digits and included in the program as part of the tool call. Thus tool number three with offset number six would be entered in the program as T0306.

Control systems always provide for more offset entry capacity than there will be tools available, so it is possible to call any offset with any tool.

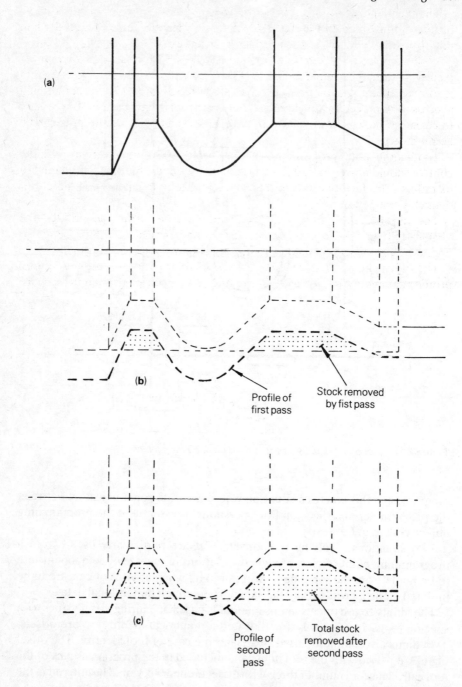

Figure 2.14 *Use of tool offsets for progressive stock removal to a set profile* **(a)** *profile detail* **(b)** *first cut* **(c)** *second cut.*

The technique of using a number of offsets to make a series of cuts along a profile is illustrated in Figure 2.14. (A similar technique can be used when milling profiles and this is discussed later in the text.)

While the use of offsets as described above is a very useful programming facility, it should be remembered that the prime objective of an offset facility is to make point programming a possibility and to simplify the programming process. The preceding text has dealt only with tool lengths. It is now necessary to consider the way in which a variety of cutter diameters and tip radii can be accommodated.

To facilitate point programming with a variety of cutters of varying radii the control should move the cutter away from the work profile a distance equal to its radius. This facility is referred to as 'cutter radius compensation' or 'cutter diameter compensation'.

The distance the cutter will actually move away from the profile—the offset—will be related to the data entry made by the machine setter or operator. The offset is activated via the appropriate program entry.

The offset can be programmed to occur to the right or left of the required profile, commonly by the use of G41 and G42 when programming in word

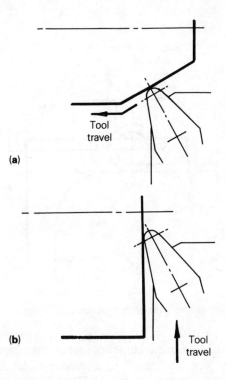

Figure 2.15 *Tool nose radius compensation (TNRC)* **(a)** *radius compensation left* **(b)** *radius compensation right.*

address mode. To determine which offset code should be programmed, the technique is to imagine being in a position looking on to the face of the tool and facing the direction of tool travel. The tool can then be visualised as being either to the right or left of the profile. It is very important to ensure that the correct offset is programmed since a move in the wrong direction may have disastrous results, particularly when large diameter cutters are being used. Tool radius to the right and left of a profile is shown in Figure 2.15.

When activating cutter radius compensation it must be ensured that the slides will first make a non-cutting move, to enable the correct tool and workpiece relationship to be established. A similar move is necessary prior to cancellation of the radius compensation. These non-cutting moves are referred to as 'ramp on' and 'ramp off' respectively.

It is now possible to return to the technique referred to earlier, of using offsets to make a series of passes along a milled profile. It is achieved by simply entering a bogus value for the cutter diameter into the control system. By making an entry that is greater than the size of the cutter being used, the actual offset activated via the program will be greater. Thus the final profile will remain oversize as illustrated in Figure 2.16. The technique can also be used to progressively remove surplus material before making a final cut.

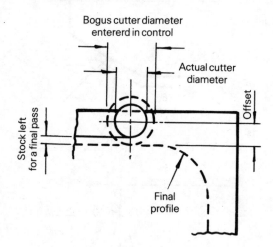

Figure 2.16 *Using an offset to create an oversize milled profile.*

The reverse application of this technique, that is, entering a value smaller than the actual cutter size, will result in a smaller offset and, in the case illustrated, an undersize component profile. Thus it is possible to produce components of varying dimensions from the same program when milling, just as it is possible to do so when turning.

Replacement tooling

For long production runs the programmer will need to give some thought to the provision of replacement tooling.

When tools need to be replaced it is possible for the setter to determine suitable offsets and make the necessary tool data entries as he would for the original tools, but this is time-consuming and interrupts production.

An alternative approach is to use replacement tooling which is identical to the original. Such identical tooling may be of two types, namely, 'qualified' or 'pre-set'.

Qualified tooling is used on turning centres and has dimensions guaranteed by the manufacturer to within ±0.08 mm from up to three datum faces.

Pre-set tooling is precisely set to predetermined dimensions in the toolroom and is applied to turning tools and milling cutters. (Further information regarding qualified and pre-set tooling is included in *An Introduction to CNC Machining,* also published by Cassell.)

The programmer may choose to recommend qualified or pre-set tools when compiling his tooling schedule, but if such tooling is prescribed the programmer may need a feedback of information from the toolroom regarding the setting sizes. This information then becomes part of the overall programming and machine-setting package and should be documented for future reference.

Tooling documentation

Documentation regarding tooling, as with machine setting instructions, may be simple or relatively complex. It depends largely on the size of the company and the degree of organisation that exists.

The possibilities range from the situation where the machine setter has personal access to the range of tooling likely to be required, to situations where the tooling is prepared in a special-purpose tool room, issued to the setter as a package for that particular job, and on completion returned to the tool room for refurbishment and storage.

For each programmed tool the minimum information required on the shop floor is as follows:

(a) programmed identity—T01, T02, T03, etc.
(b) tool type;
(c) holder type and size;
(d) insert type and size;
(e) overall dimensions (solid tools).

When pre-setting is involved the toolroom personnel usually determine the original pre-set dimensions. The sizes should ultimately be notified to the part programmer so that they may be recorded and included as part of the general documentation for that particular job. A well-organised tool preparation facility may well retain the data against their own job reference to facilitate the preparation of replacement tooling, and to allow for the possibility of having to prepare identical tools at some future time.

When tooling offsets are being used to achieve a particular machining effect, as discussed on page 59, the value of the offsets must be included on the document.

It is often the situtation that information regarding tooling, and sometimes information relating to machine setting, is included on the original part program form when one is used. Information documented in this way is of necessity rather brief, but in many cases is adequate.

Another practice widely adopted is to give tooling details alongside the tool call in the part program. Again, the information is brief but adequate for many situations.

The important thing is that the part programmer fully appreciates the needs of the people more directly concerned with the machining operation. There must be an efficient transfer of the relevant information. The means adopted to achieve this objective will vary, but the programmer should always remember that it is a very important aspect of his or her work.

Calculations

It could be argued that, in a well-organised CNC machining environment, the people responsible for the production of the detail drawings of the components to be machined should appreciate the needs of the part programmer and ensure that the drawings are dimensioned accordingly. For example, it is of considerable help when positional slide movements are to be programmed in absolute mode if all dimensions on the drawing are given in relation to a suitable datum. This is especially valuable when the programming technique involves conversational manual data input, since the last thing a programmer wants to do is to interrupt his thought process in order to calculate unspecified dimensions.

However, whatever the ideal situation may be, it is almost certain that eventually the part programmer will be confronted with a detail drawing that does not cater for his or her requirements. He or she will then find it necessary to make calculations and add dimensions, and perhaps in some cases to completely redimension the drawing.

(The reader should differentiate between poor industrial practice and situations with which he or she may be deliberately confronted in a learning situation, where the objective will be to provide an understanding of the problems likely to be encountered in practice.)

Mention has already been made of the need for dimensions to be given in relation to a set datum when absolute programming is to be used. The opposite situation could also arise, whereby the dimensions are stated in relation to a datum but the programmer needs to program incremental slide moves. In this case the stated dimensions will need to be sub-divided. The programmer should exercise caution in this particular situation, and ensure that such an approach is acceptable from a design point of view; minor errors on each of a series of incremental moves could, due to inaccuracies in the machine movement, accumulate into a larger error that would be unacceptable.

There are other situations which are more complex than simply converting absolute dimensions to incremental and vice versa. Two of these in particular are the need to determine:

(a) profile intersection points;
(b) the location of arc centres.

However complex the profile or shape of a machined surface may appear to be, it can be broken down and defined geometrically as a number of intersecting straight lines or arcs or a combination of the two. To program appropriate machine slide movements the programmer is required to determine this geometry, and translate production of the profile into a series of linear or circular movements.

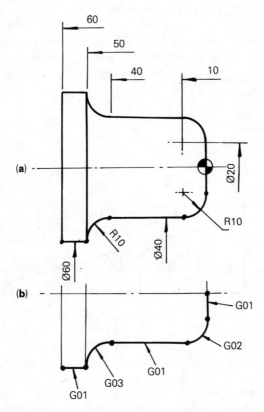

Figure 2.17 *Geometric elements of a profile* **(a)** *component detail* **(b)** *profile definition.*

Thus to finish machine the profile shown in Figure 2.17 the following movements will be necessary:

Move 1   Linear
Move 2   Circular, clockwise
Move 3   Linear
Move 4   Circular, counter-clockwise
Move 5   Linear

If word address programming is being used these moves can be described using the appropriate G code: G01, G02, G01, G03 and G01. It may be helpful to mark the drawing accordingly, as in the illustration.

The reader will already appreciate that when programming positional moves, whether they are linear or circular, the target position has to be numerically defined. In this particular example, because the component is dimensioned correctly and the arcs are conveniently 90°, the target position, that is, the intersection points of the geometrical elements of the profile, are readily discerned. No further calculations are necessary.

Consider now the component shown in Figure 2.18(a). Although it is a relatively simple profile, from a programming point of view the drawing is not as helpful as it might be. The target position of the arc, that is, the point at which the circular move ends and the linear move commences, is not defined. Calculations are required as follows in order to determine the target position in the X and Z axes.

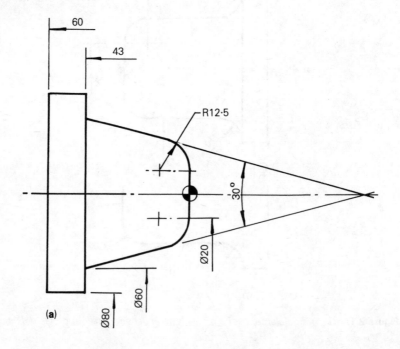

Figure 2.18 **(a)** *component detail*

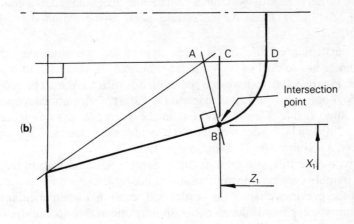

Figure 2.18 (b) *profile intersection calculation.*

In Figure 2.18b:

$\emptyset$ $X_1 = 2(CB + 10)$ and $Z_1 = CD$

In triangle ABC:

$A\hat{B}C = 15°$ and $AB = 12.5$

1. To calculate CB:

$$\text{Cos } A\hat{B}C = \frac{CB}{AB}$$

$$\begin{aligned} CB &= \text{Cos } A\hat{B}C \times AB \\ &= \text{Cos } 15 \times 12.5 \\ &= 0.966 \times 12.5 \\ &= 12.074 \end{aligned}$$

$\emptyset$ $X_1 = 2(12.074 + 10) = 44.148$

2. To calculate AC:

$$\text{Sin } A\hat{B}C = \frac{AC}{AB}$$

$$\begin{aligned} AC &= \text{Sin } A\hat{B}C \times AB \\ &= \text{Sin } 15 \times 12.5 \\ &= 0.259 \times 12.5 \\ &= 3.235 \end{aligned}$$

Since $Z_1 = CD$ then $\begin{aligned} Z_1 &= AD - AC \\ &= 12.5 - 3.235 \\ &= 9.265 \end{aligned}$

Thus the target position, with the X value being programmed as a diameter, is X44.148 Z−9.265. These values would need to be included in the part program.

This particular calculation is fairly typical of the situations the part programmer has to deal with. A similar situation presents itself in the profile shown in Figure 2.19(a) where one radius blends with another. The problem is: where does one radius end and the second one start? Calculations are necessary to determine the location of point P in the X and Y axes as indicated in Figure 2.19(b). The reader may like to consider the solution to the problem. (Answers: 47.81 mm and 71.25 mm respectively.)

This type of profile also presents the second type of calculation referred to earlier, namely determining the location of arc centres.

From the previous chapter the reader will recall that when circular arcs are programmed using word address programming one of three techniques may be involved. All require the target positions to be identified but the radius definition varies. The first involves defining the arc centre in relation to the program datum, and the second requires the arc centre to be defined in relation to the arc starting position. The third method simply requires the value of the radius.

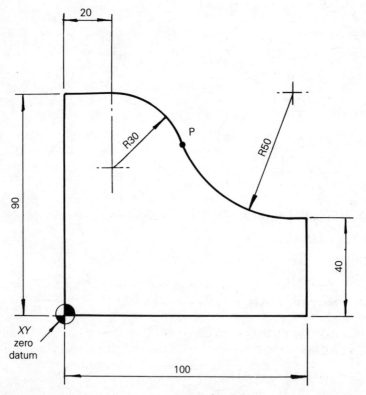

Figure 2.19 (a) *profile detail*

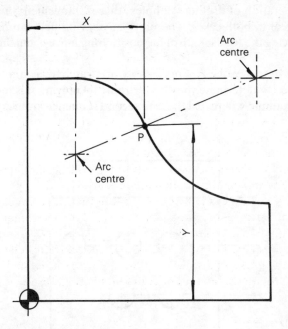

Figure 2.19 (b) *required profile intersection dimensions.*

Using the first method, the centre of the 30 mm radius arc is easily determined from the dimensions already on the drawing. But the location of the centre of the 50 mm radius is not so straightforward and a calculation is required.

Using the second method of circular interpolation the definition of the arc centres in relation to the start points again presents a problem as far as the 50 mm radius is concerned, and a calculation will be necessary before the program can be written.

Exercises involving the calculation of profile intersection points and arc centres are included in Chapter 4, 'Part Programming Calculations'.

Tool paths

A prime objective of the part programmer should be to ensure that a component is machined in the shortest possible time. Earlier in the text reference was made to the way a well-planned sequence of machining operations can contribute to this objective. But often within each individual machining sequence there is room for further efficiency which results in time saving.

Consider the drilling of the series of five holes in the component shown in Figure 2.20. Two sequences in which the holes might be drilled are indicated. Which sequence would be the quicker?

The actual operation of drilling the holes, that is, movement in the Z axis, would be identical in both cases. Therefore any saving that can be achieved must be by reducing the total length of the positioning moves, and therefore the time taken.

Providing the detail drawing is reasonably accurately drawn a simple rule check may suffice to determine the shorter route. Applying this technique to this particular example will reveal that the second sequence is quicker than the first.

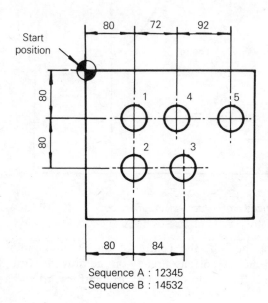

Sequence A : 12345
Sequence B : 14532

Figure 2.20 *Alternative drilling sequences.*

The need to give careful consideration to toolpaths is also important during stock removal operations. This is particularly so when there are no stock removal canned cycles available within the control system, or if they cannot be utilised in a particular situation.

Consider the removal of stock, or area clearance as it is also known, in order to machine the step shown in Figure 2.21.

If a pocket milling cycle is available on the control system of the machine this could be used, the missing sides of the 'pocket' being indicated by the dotted line. Use of the cycle would ensure that efficient tool paths are employed.

If such a cycle is not available then the matter becomes a little more complex. The process of producing the step will involve programming a series of linear moves, with careful attention being given to providing an appropriate cutter overlap to ensure a clean face. The lengths of relative cutter travel will also have to ensure a uniform amount of metal is left for a cleaning pass along the profile. The programmer should also ensure that the cutter paths used are the shortest and therefore the quickest.

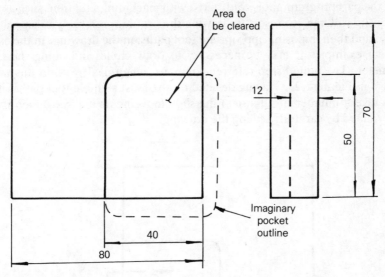

Figure 2.21 *'Pocket' detail.*

Similar problems often present themselves during turning operations. Figure 2.22 shows a typical example.

There is no short cut when solving this type of problem. After a little experience of dealing with situations of this nature the trainee programmer soon comes to appreciate the value of canned cycles, which reduce the amount of machining dealt with in this manner to a minimum.

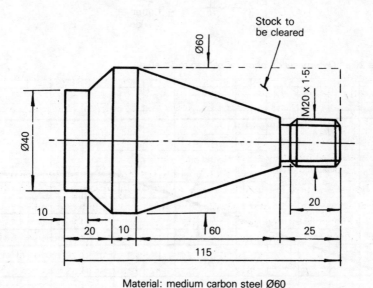

Material: medium carbon steel Ø60

Figure 2.22 *Component requiring excess stock removal.*

If the part programmer is confronted with machining situations such as these he or she will have to resort to drawing the profile, preferably to an enlarged scale, and then imposing appropriate tool paths on the drawing. In the case of milling examples it may be necessary to draw circles indicating the cutter diameter. The milled step referred to above, when dealt with in this way, is shown in Figure 2.23. Having decided on the most suitable tool paths (which may take a number of attempts) the slide movements may be dimensionally determined by carefully scaling the drawing.

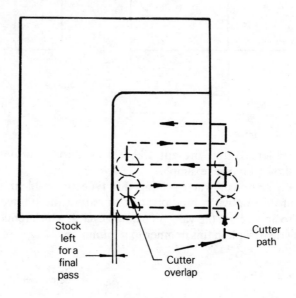

Figure 2.23 *Determination of cutter path to mill a step.*

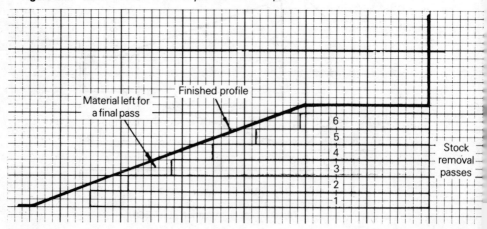

Figure 2.24 *Determination of tool paths when turning.*

An alternative approach is to reproduce the profile on graph paper, as shown in Figure 2.24, in which case the graduated lines on the graph paper can be used to determine the dimensional value of the necessary moves.

Exercises involving the determination of cutter paths are included in Chapter 4, 'Part Programming Calculations'.

Cutting speeds and feeds

It is difficult to determine precise data for any metal-cutting operation without knowledge of the practicalities involved. For example: the condition of the machine, the power available, the rigidity of tooling and work-holding arrangements, the volume of metal to be removed, the surface finish required and the type of coolant to be used are all factors which have to be considered when determining the appropriate speeds and feeds to be employed.

People concerned with programming, as opposed to setting and operating, sometimes lack such practical experience. Nevertheless, the programmer is obliged to make program entries that will be, if not perfect, then at least functional.

Should it prove that the programmed speed and feed are inappropriate, machine control units have manually operated override facilities to enable the operator to increase or decrease speeds and feeds as machining proceeds. If such action is found to be necessary the programmer should be informed so that the part program can be modified accordingly.

The selection of appropriate speeds and feeds can be based on experience when the programmer possesses the necessary practical background. Long-serving craftsmen often develop an instinctive ability to recognise the correct speed and feed for any particular machining task, having long forgotten any theoretical basis they may have once been taught concerning such matters. But this approach is perhaps more suitable to conventional machining processes than it is to CNC machining.

Reference to data published by the manufacturers of the cutting tools to be used is more appropriate for numerically controlled machining, since the lack of operator involvement that is a feature of machining in this way makes it imperative that the optimum speeds and feeds are used. However, when reference is made to published data the programmer should exercise caution. The figures quoted, while perfectly feasible when employed under the correct conditions, can appear to be somewhat optimistic when applied to many machining situations. Examples of manufacturers' data relating to cutting speeds and feeds are included in Appendices 2, 3 and 4.

Whatever approach is used it is essential that the programmer fully appreciates the capabilities of any machine for which he or she is preparing programs. For instance, it is pointless to program speeds and feeds that result in metal removal rates that are beyond the power capacity of the machine. Conversely, it is equally pointless to underuse the power available. If a programmer lacks essential knowledge of this nature then liaison with those who have had practical experience of the machine should be a priority.

Unusual machining situations involving set-ups that may lack rigidity should be approached with care, and the programmed speeds and feeds should be initially on the low side. They can always be increased later in the light of experience gained at the machine when metal cutting has actually taken place.

Special attention should also be given to specific requirements regarding surface finish. Machinists are often obsessed with obtaining a 'good' finish but it should be remembered that there is no point in reducing metal removal rates to obtain a high-quality surface finish that is not necessary. A further point to remember is that a designer may specifically require a 'rough' finish, so it is essential to work to the information contained on the drawing. The programmer should ensure that the setter/operator responsible for the machining operation fully appreciates what the requirements are.

The intricate contouring capabilities of CNC machines can also present problems regarding surface finish. For example, feed rate which produces satisfactory results when machining a parallel turned surface may no longer produce acceptable results when the cutting tool changes direction to machine a tapered or radial surface. Similar situations present themselves during milling operations. When machining complex profiles that are subject to stringent surface finish requirements the results obtained from programmed feeds and speeds, particularly feeds, should be monitored and modifications made if necessary.

Surface finish is, of course, affected by the condition of the cutting tool. Tool performance begins to deteriorate from the moment the tool is first used, and ultimately it not only affects the surface finish but may result in dimensional features not being maintained, unacceptable vibration, work deflection and eventually total failure of the tool. An unsuitable choice of cutting speeds and feeds may hasten this process, so the part programmer must give due consideration to tool life when making decisions in this respect.

It is possible to calculate the life of a cutting tool. The formula used for this purpose was derived by experimentation and, because of the many variables that exist between one machining situation and another, the results obtained from its application can only be used as a guide. The reader may reasonably ask why bother to make such a calculation if the result is only a guide, and it would be difficult to give a totally convincing answer. Nevertheless it would be helpful to know when a tool was reaching the end of its life, so that replacement could be effected before total failure occurred. The automatic tool condition sensing devices being applied to the more complex CNC machining installations may provide the answer. In the meantime, how is the part programmer to decide what speeds and feeds to use to give an acceptable tool life, while at the same time achieving the basic objective of removing metal in the least possible time?

As stated earlier, reference can be made to the cutting tool manufacturers' literature. Their figures will have taken into account the fact that a reasonable tool life is required by the user of their products. But there is still the problem that local conditions may make their recommendations invalid. Yet again, it may be initially necessary to rely on past practical experience, and to be prepared to make modifications based on a reasoned appraisal of the situation when metal cutting is under way.

One further point relating to tool performance should be noted. The chip-breaking qualities of most carbide-tipped tools is directly related to speeds and feeds. If swarf clearance becomes a problem some modification of the cutting conditions may be appropriate.

Spindle speeds

The program data controlling spindle speeds is expressed in one of two ways, the numerical value in both cases being preceded by the letter S. Thus a data entry of, say, S250 could indicate either a *constant surface cutting speed* of 250 metres per minute (m/min) or, alternatively, a *spindle speed* of 250 revolutions per minute (rev/min).

All machines have the facility to program a set spindle speed in revolutions per minute, while the alternative facility of programming a constant surface cutting speed is now commonly available on the majority of turning centres.

When both facilities are available the machine controller differentiates between the two possibilities via a previous data entry that will establish the desired operating mode. In the case of word address programming this mode is established by a G code entry, commonly G96 (m/min) and G97 (rev/min). An alternative G code may be used when the cutting speed entry is to be interpreted as feet per minute (ft/min). In the case of conversational MDI the mode is established by selection from the displayed options.

Consider the process of programming a constant surface cutting speed. The cutting speed is the rate at which the cutting tool passes over the workpiece material, or alternatively the rate at which the material is travelling as it passes the cutting tool. As indicated above, it can be expressed in either metres or feet per minute.

Appropriate surface cutting speeds for use with cutting tools made of specific materials, when used to cut certain metals, have been determined by experiment. The figures give due regard to the maximum metal removal rates that can be obtained, while at the same time equating satisfactorily with other factors such as tool life, surface finish and power consumption. These recommended cutting speeds are published by the manufacturers of cutting tools as a guide to users of their products (see Appendices 2, 3 and 4). As stated earlier, it may be necessary to modify these values to suit local conditions before making a program entry.

The advantage of programming a surface cutting speed as opposed to a set spindle speed in revolutions per minute is best appreciated by considering the simple operation of parting-off from bar stock during a turning operation.

During a parting-off operation the diameter of the work where metal cutting is actually taking place is steadily decreasing, and therefore the cutting efficiency is only maintained if the spindle speed increases at a corresponding rate. This steady increase, which maintains the most efficient metal cutting rate for that particular job material, is automatically achieved via the constant surface cutting speed programming facility.

The process of parting off is a convenient one to explain the value of the constant surface cutting speed programming. However, it is not a process where the use of such a facility is absolutely critical. The facility is more likely to be of value during the turning of complex profiles requiring a uniformly high standard of surface finish throughout the turned length.

In order to program a constant spindle speed in revolutions per minute, it is necessary to make a simple calculation that takes into consideration the recommended surface cutting speed referred to above, and also the diameter of the workpiece in the case of turning operations, or the cutter in the case of milling operations. The relationship between these factors is expressed as follows:

$$\text{Spindle rev/min} = \frac{1000 \times \text{Cutting speed in m/min}}{\pi \times \text{Work or cutter diameter in mm}}$$

Multiplying the cutting speed by 1000 converts it from *metres* per minute to *millimetres* per minute, while multiplying the work or cutter diameter by π, that is, calculating the circumference, determines the relative linear travel per revolution in millimetres. Dividing the circumference in millimetres into the cutting speed in millimetres per minute determines the number of revolutions per minute required.

When inch programming, the relationship between spindle speed, work or cutter diameter and the required cutting speed is expressed as follows:

$$\text{Spindle speed in rev/min} = \frac{12 \times \text{Cutting speed in ft/min}}{\pi \times \text{Work or cutter diameter in inches}}$$

In this case multiplying the cutting speed by 12 and so converting it to ins/min makes all the units in the equation compatible.

Exercises involving the calculation of spindle speeds are included in Chapter 4, 'Part Programming Calculations'.

A number of cutting tool manufacturers distribute simple calculators, the use of which eliminates the need to make calculations. These devices will indicate the appropriate cutting tool material, selected from the manufacturer's range, that should be used when machining a certain material type, together with a recommended surface cutting speed for the type of operation (roughing or finishing) that is to be undertaken.

Feed rates

The calculators referred to above will also indicate an appropriate feed rate for the operation. The feed rate is the speed at which the cutter penetrates into the work material.

When programming data relating to feed rate it can be expressed either as millimetres per minute (mm/min) or millimetres per revolution (mm/rev) of the machine spindle. With inch programming the units will be inches per minute (ins/min) or inches per revolution (ins/rev).

The letter F is commonly used to denote the feed rate in a part program. Thus F25 could indicate a feed rate of 0.25 mm/rev while F80 could indicate a feed rate of 80 mm/min, depending on the mode of expression being used. It is necessary to ensure that the data entered and the programming mode are compatible.

Although variations exist, the set-up data using the G codes common to a number or word address programming systems are as follows:

G93	mm/min
G95	mm/rev
G92	ins/min
G94	ins/rev

Also used are:

G94	feed/min
G95	feed/rev

In this second situation the units to be used are established by the use of G70 for inch and G71 for metric.

Feed rates are published by cutting tool manufacturers in the same way as surface cutting speeds. Usually the rates are expressed as mm/rev or ins/rev. To convert to mm/min or ins/min involves making a simple calculation as follows:

Feed mm/min = Feed mm/rev × Spindle speed rev/min

or alternatively:

Feed ins/min = Feed ins/rev × Spindle speed rev/min

The manufacturers of milling cutters sometimes quote recommended feed rates in millimetres or inches per tooth, in which case it is necessary, prior to making the above calculation, to determine the feed per revolution of the cutter. This is achieved as follows:

Feed/rev = Feed/tooth × Number of cutter teeth.

Examples and exercises involving the calculation of feed rates using published data are included in Chapter 4, 'Part Programming Calculations'.

Program listing and proving

Before starting to list a part program all the various facets of competent part programming discussed so far should have received due attention.

The sequence of operations, together with the tooling and work-holding techniques to be employed, should be documented. Appropriate speeds and feed rates should have been determined and all the necessary calculations affecting slide movements must be complete.

Having reached this stage the way is clear to list the program, and this requires the programmer to be conversant with the machine programming language.

To become fully proficient with a particular programming system takes time and practice. As with most things it is a case of starting with relatively simple tasks and gradually progressing to more complex examples. If you are a student, or perhaps undergoing training in an industrial establishment, it is almost certain that your course work will be structured in this way.

Competent part programming demands a logical approach and a high degree of concentration and care when actually listing the program. Mistakes are easily made and can have disastrous results, although fortunately most mistakes can be discovered and rectified before machining takes place.

Programs may be listed on appropriate forms, on plain paper or be entered into a computer and listed on the display screen. Programs initially hand-written can, of course, also be entered into a computer and visually displayed.

The use of a computer for program listing is often coupled with the facility to prove the program using animated computer graphics. This involves, in effect, 'machining' the component on the screen.

The effectiveness of proving programs in this way will depend on the sophistication of the software available. The simplest software will usually highlight major errors such as movement occurring in the wrong direction or a lathe tool crashing into a chuck, while the more complex will also indicate errors relating to speeds and feeds and even the absence of a coolant supply.

Ultimately, the part program wil be entered into the machine control unit, but this may also involve computer graphics. Figure 2.25 shows a controller that includes a built-in VDU. As the program is entered the screen will display the geometric profile of the part and the programmed cutter paths and thus confirm, or otherwise, the validity of the data input. The illustration relates to a program written for the part detailed in Figure 2.26. An enlargement of the VDU display is shown in Figure 2.27 where the component profile can be more readily defined.

A large number of machines currently in use do not have the benefit of built-in computer graphics, and if off-line computer graphics proving facilities are not available then the proving of the part program must take the form of a test run and/or a dry run.

The test run is basically a check that the data input is valid, that is, that the machine is capable of responding to the data entries included in the program. Data errors are usually indicated by a displayed message. No slide movement takes place during the test run.

The dry run procedure also excludes metal cutting, but with this checking procedure slide movements occur at a rapid rate of traverse. This test ensures that the intended machine movements are occurring, and that they will result in the machined features required.

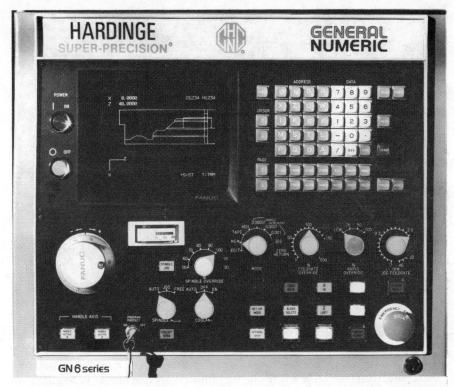

Figure 2.25 *Photo. A machine controller with built-in VDU to facilitate program proving.*

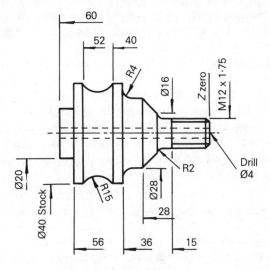

Material: aluminium alloy Ø40

Figure 2.26 *Component detail.*

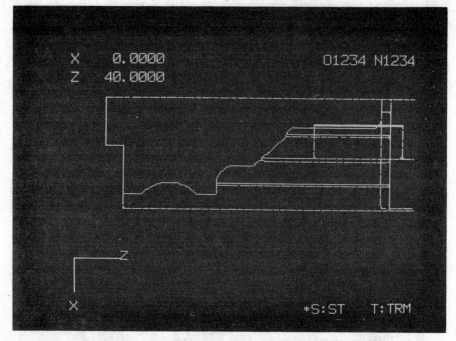

Figure 2.27 *An enlargement of the VDU display shown in Figure 2.25.*

A further test available even on the simplest of machines, is to run the program through at the programmed feed rates, but without the job material being in position so that no machining actually takes place.

Tests of this nature carried out on the machine may or may not be the responsibility of the programmer, although he or she will soon be involved if any errors are indicated.

Finally, there is the need, particularly in industrial situations, to record the program for future use. In its simplest form, storage can be a hand-written version of the proved program. Alternatively, it may be in the form of a perforated tape or be recorded on a magnetic tape or disc.

Whatever the storage medium it must be remembered that people looking to re-use the program at a later date will also need information relating to tooling and work-holding. This information is as critical as the part program and must also be carefully filed for future reference.

Manual part programming examples

The programming examples which follow were prepared by different people, each fully conversant with the programming systems and the capabilities of the machines indicated.

The programs are for the components detailed in Figures 2.26 and 2.28 respectively. They are included to convey an appreciation of the variations that exist between programming languages and also, to a lesser extent, the practical variations in approach that are adopted by different people even when the program is for a relatively simple workpiece.

The programs have all been compiled using word address languages. However, it should be noted that the Hurco KMB is primarily a conversational MDI machine. A simple data input operation, via a magnetic tape, instantly converts the control to word address mode; thus both programming techniques are available on one machine.

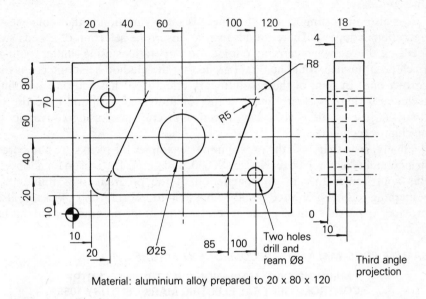

Material: aluminium alloy prepared to 20 x 80 x 120

Figure 2.28 *Component detail.*

A study of the program listings will indicate to the reader that while there are some similarities there are also considerable variations between the illustrated languages. An interesting exercise is to identify a particular operation—this is easily done by noting where a tool change occurs—and then to make a comparison between programs. For example, look at the screw cutting operation for each of the turning programs. It will be seen that the data entries in each program bear little resemblance to each other.

Another interesting comparison to make is between the circular interpolation data contained in each of the milling programs. Both use the G02, or G2, code, and both identify the target position in the X and Y axes. But it will be seen that the definition of the radius is different in each case.

Some of the variations observed will not result from the use of different programming languages. Some may be owing to the fact that each programmer has approached the task in an individual way. For instance, in one case all the machining associated with the outside profile of the turned component was programmed to be carried out with just one tool. The second programmer elected to rough turn the part first, using a second tool for a finishing operation.

Both techniques are capable of producing a perfect component. The reader may like to consider the circumstances when the use of one method might be preferable to the other.

Regarding the milling example, it will be seen that one programmer has called for the use of more carbide-tipped tooling than the other programmer. The use of carbide-tipped tooling would, of course, result in a shorter machining time, but it is possible that the second programmer did not have access to suitable tipped tooling and so the approach adopted had to take this into consideration.

It is also interesting to note that there is some variation in the sequence of operations adopted. There are also variations in the selection of speeds and feeds used even when carrying out identical operations using similar tooling. Each programmer would no doubt argue that the method he adopted was the correct one! In spite of the revolutionary effect CNC has had on machining techniques there is clearly much scope for individual skill and expertise to flourish, just as there always has been with craftsmen using conventional machining techniques.

Finally, note that in all the programming examples the blocks are numbered in increments of ten: N0010, N0020, N0030, and so on. The reason for adopting this approach is that if, on completion of the program, it is found that something has been omitted if will be possible to insert further blocks. It also provides space that will facilitate general editing of the program should this be found to be necessary.

SAMPLE PROGRAM No. 1 FOR COMPONENT FIGURE 2.26

MACHINE TYPE: HARDINGE HXL TURNING CENTRE
CONTROL : GENERAL ELECTRIC MARK CENTURY 1050

Tooling layout

T101	35° light turning and facing tool
T202	1 mm pitch ISO threading tool
T303	Grooving tool 5 mm wide
T404	Parting tool
T1111	No. 2 HSS centre drill
T1212	Long series 4 mm Ø drill

Part program

```
N0010    G71
N0020    G40
N0030    G95
N0040    G97    S1000   M03
N0050    G00
N0060    G53    X117.8   Z254   T00
N0070    M01
N0100    G25    P₁10 P₂60
N0110    G41    T100 (light turning and facing tool)
N0120    G54    X44    Z0    T101    M08
N0130    G92    R44    S3000
N0140    G96    S250   F.2
```

```
N0150      G01 X-1
N0160      G00   X44   Z2.25
N0170      G68   X12   Z0   I.25   K.25   P₁900   P₂950   P₃1.5   P₄-0
N0180      G00   Z-40
N0190      G01   X40
N0200      G02   X13.747   Z-16   I12
N0210      G02   X40   Z-52   K12
N0220      G00   X44
N0230      G25   P₁10   P₂70
N0310      T1100 (centre drill)
N0320      G54   X0   Z3   T1111   M08
N0330      S2500   F.1
N0340      G01   Z-6
N0350      G00   Z3
N0360      G25   P₁10   P₂70
N0400      T1200 (HSS Ø4 drill)
N0410      G54   X0   Z3   T1212   M08
N0420      S2000   F.2
N0430      G83   Z-60   P₁10   P₂.8   P₅4
N0440      G25   P₁10   P₂70
N0500      T200 (screw cutting tool)
N0510      G54   X16   Z3   T0202
N0520      S1500   M08
N0530      G84   X10.773   Z-15   P₁.05   P₂1
N0540      G25   P₁10   P₂70
N0600      T300   (grooving tool)
N0610      G54   X44   Z-56   T303   M08
N0620      G92   R44   S2000
N0630      G96   S150   F.1
N0640      G01   X20
N0650      G00   X44
N0660      G25   P₁10   P₂70
N0700      T400 (parting tool)
N0710      G54   X44   Z-60   T404   M08
N0720      G92   R44   S2000
N0730      G96   S150   F.1
N0740      G01   X0
N0750      G00   X44
N0760      G25   P₁10   P₂70
N0770      M30
N0900      G00   X12   Z0
N0910      G64   Z-21   P₁2
N0920      G01   X28   Z-28
N0930      G64   Z-36   P₁4
N0940      G01   X40
N0950      G00   X44
%
```

SAMPLE PROGRAM No. 2 FOR COMPONENT FIGURE 2.26

MACHINE TYPE: NAKAMURA SUPERTURN 2
CONTROL : FANUC 6TB

Tooling layout

T101	80° rough turning tool
T202	6 mm dia. NC spotting drill
T303	35° finish turning tool
T404	4 mm dia. long series drill
T505	1 mm pitch ISO threading tool
T707	5 mm wide o/dia grooving tool
T909	Parting tool

Part program

N10	G00 G21 G40 G96 G99
N20	G28 U0 W0
N30	G0 U0 W0 (set index position — X200. Z200)
N40	G50 X200. Z200. S3500
N50	M42
N60	G97 S2000 T100 M3 (R. turn)
N70	G0 X45. Z.1 T101 M8
N80	G1 G96 X - 1.8 F.25
N90	G0 X45. Z2
N100	G71 P110 Q230 U.3 W.15 D300 F.25
N110	G0 X9. Z2
N120	Z.1
N130	X10
N140	X12. Z-2
N150	Z-19
N160	G2 X16. Z-21. R2
N170	G1 X28. Z-28
N180	Z-32
N190	G2 X36. Z-36. R4
N200	G1 X40
N210	Z-66
N220	X45
N230	G00 Z2
N240	G97 X200. Z200. T100
N250	G97 S3200 T200 M3 (spot drill)
N260	G0 X0 Z3. T202 M8
N270	G1 G98 Z-2. F100
N280	G0 G99 Z3
N290	X200. Z200. T200
N300	G97 S4500 T400 M3 (4 mm drill)
N310	G0 G98 X0 Z3. T404 M8
N320	G74 Z-63. K3. F100
N330	G99 G0 X200. Z200. T400
N340	G97 S2000 T300 M3 (f. turn)
N350	G0 X3. Z2. T303 M8
N360	GL G96 Z0. F.1
N370	X10
N380	X12. Z-2

```
N390      Z-19
N400      G2 X16. Z-21. R2
N410      G1 X28. Z-28
N420      Z-32
N430      G2 X36. Z-36. R4
N440      G1 X40
N450      Z-40
N460      G2 X40. Z-52. R15
N470      Z-66
N450      X45
N460      G0 G97 X200. Z200. T300
N470      G97 S2000 T500 M3 (o/dia thread)
N480      G0 X16. Z10. T505 M8
N490      G76 X 10.2 Z-15. K.54 D150 F1. A60
N500      G0 X200. Z200. T500
N510      G97 S2500 T700 M3 (o/dia groove)
N520      G0 X45. Z-61. T707 M8
N530      G1 X20. F.15
N540      G4 X.02
N550      G0 X45
N560      X200. Z200. T700

N570      G97 S2500 T900 M3 (part off)
N580      G0 X45. Z-65. T909 M8
N590      G1 X0 F.15
N600      G0 X45
N610      X200. Z200. T900
N620      M30
%
```

SAMPLE PROGRAM No. 1 FOR COMPONENT FIGURE 2.28

MACHINE TYPE: OKUMA HOWA MILLAC 4VA
CONTROL : FANUC 6MB

Tooling layout

T1	100 mm dia. carbide insert facemill
T2	25 mm dia. carbide insert 'U' drill
T3	20 mm dia. brazed carbide end mill
T4	10 mm dia. HSS end mill
T5	6 mm dia. N.C. spotting drill
T6	7.6 mm dia. HSS drill
T7	8 mm dia. reamer

Part program

```
N 10      G00 G17 G21 G40 G49 G80 G90 G98
N 20      G54 T1
N 30      M6 (100 mm dia. facemill)
N 40      G90 G0 X-60. Y40. S350 M3 T2
N 50      G43 Z0 H1 M8
N 60      G1 X180. F150
N 70      G0 Z5. M9
N 80      G28 G91 X0 Y0 Z0 M5
N 90      M6 (25 mm U. drill)
```

```
N100    G0 G90 X60. Y40. S1200 M3 T3
N110    G43 Z3. H2 M8
N120    G81 G99 R3. Z-22. F150
N130    G80 M9
N140    G28 G91 X0 Y0 Z0 M5
N150    M6 (20 mm end mill)
N160    G90 G0 X-12. Y.12. S1600 M3 T4
N170    G43 Z-4. H3 M8
N180    G1 G41 X-10. D21 F250
N190    Y62
N200    G2 X18. Y70. R8
N210    G1 X102
N220    G2 X110. Y62. R8
N230    G1 Y18
N240    G2 X102. Y10. R8
N250    G1 X18
N260    G2 X10. Y18. R8
N250    G1 Y20
N260    G40 X-12. M9
N270    G0 Z5
N280    X60. Y40
N290    Z-10
N300    G1 G41 Y20. F200 D22
N310    X20
N320    X40. Y60
N330    X100
N340    X85. Y20
N350    X60
N360    G40 Y40
N370    G0 Z5. M9
N380    G28 G91 X0 Y0 Z0 M5
N390    M6 (10 mm end mill)
N400    G90 G0 X60. Y40. S800 M3 T5
N410    G43 Z-10. H4 M8
N420    G1 G41 Y20. F150 D23
N430    X20
N440    X40.Y60
N450    X100
N460    X85. Y20
N470    X60
N480    G40 Y40
N490    G0 Z5. M9
N500    G28 G91 X0 Y0 Z0 M5
N510    M6 (6 mm spot drill)
N520    G0 G90 X20. Y60. S1600 M3 T6
N530    G43 Z3. H5 M8
N540    G81 G99 R3. Z-2. F100
N550    X100. Y20
N560    G80 M9
N570    G28  G91 X0 Y0 Z0 M5
N580    M6 (7.6 mm drill)
N590    G90 G0 X20. Y60. S1250 M3 T7
N600    G43 Z3. H6 M8
N610    G73 G99 R3. Z-25. Q3. F100
```

```
N620      X100. Y20
N630      G80 M9
N640      G28 G91 X0 Y0 Z0 M5
N650      M6 (8 mm reamer)
N660      G0 G90 X20. Y60. S590 M3
N670      G43 Z3. H7 M8
N680      G85 G99 R3. Z-25. F100
N690      X100. Y20
N700      G80 M9
N710      G28 G19 X0 Y0 Z0 M5
N720      G90 M30
%
```

SAMPLE PROGRAM No. 2 FOR COMPONENT FIGURE 2.28

MACHINE TYPE: HURCO KMB MILLING MACHINE
CONTROL: HURCO

Tooling layout

T1	50 mm dia. carbide insert facemill
T2	7.5 mm dia. HSS drill
T3	8 mm dia. reamer
T4	25 mm dia. carbide insert drill
T5	10 mm dia. HSS end mill

Part program

```
N5        G0 G71 G90 X-30 Y-30 S400 T1 M6 (50 mm dia. facemill)
N10       Z-2 M3
N15       Y20
N20       G1 X150 F150
N25       G0 Y60
N30       G1 X-30
N35       G0 Y-30
N40       S1300 T2 M6 (7.5 mm dia. drill)
N45       G81 X20 Y60 Z24 F100 M3
N50       X60 Y40
N55       X100 Y20
N60       G0 X-30 Y-30
N65       S500 T3 M6 (8 mm dia. reamer)
N70       G81 X20 Y60 Z24 F80 M3
N75       X100 Y20
N80       G0 X-30 Y-30
N85       S400 T4 M6 (25 mm dia. drill)
N90       G81 X60 Y40 Z22 F140 M3
N95       G0 X-30 Y-30
N100      S1000 T5 M6 (10 mm dia. end mill)
N105      G41 X10 Z-6 M3
N110      G1 Y62 F155
N115      G2 X18 Y70 I18 J62
N120      G1 X102
N125      G2 X110 Y62 I102 J62
N130      G1 Y18
N135      G2 X102 I102 J18
N140      G1 X18
```

N145	G2 X10 Y18 I18 J18
N150	G1 Y30
N155	G0 Z0
N160	G40 X60 Y40
N165	G42 G1 Z-12
N170	Y60
N175	X100
N180	X85 Y20
N185	X20
N190	X40 Y60
N195	X91
N200	X76 Y29
N205	X29
N210	X49 Y51
N215	X81
N220	X66 Y39
N225	X39
N230	X59 Y45
N235	G0 Z2
N240	G40 X-30 Y-30
N245	M2

Questions

1 Describe two basic planning considerations which facilitate producing a part in the shortest possible time.

2 Explain what is meant by 'multi-directional' cutting forces and suggest techniques that a programmer should consider in order to eliminate their effect.

3 Explain what is meant by a 'floating zero' and state the advantages of such a facility.

4 With the aid of a simple sketch, or sketches, describe a situation where two programmed zero shifts would be required during the production of a turned part.

5 Assuming a situation where the part programmer is not in close contact with the machine shop, what documentation should be prepared to facilitate the transfer of essential information between the two activities of programming and production?

6 Explain how the tool offset facility can be used to program a series of cuts along a turned profile using the same programmed slide movements for each pass.

7 Suggest one method each for keeping (i) tool indexing time, and (ii) slide movement to a minimum and state why this should be a programming objective.

8   With the aid of a simple sketch describe what is meant by 'tool nose radius compensation' and describe a practical approach that can be employed to determine whether the required compensation is to the right or left of a profile.

9   Describe an approach that could be used to determine suitable roughing passes when turning a complex profile on a machine where the control does not include an appropriate stock removal cycle.

10   Describe in detail the methods that can be used to prove a part program.

3

COMPUTER-AIDED PART PROGRAMMING

The application and advantages of CAPP

When NC, as opposed to CNC, was first introduced, the only way a curve could be produced was by approximation, making a series of angular moves using slide movements in two axes which, when blended together, approximated to the curve required. The larger the number of small angular movements made, the more precise the final curve.

On the face of it this would appear to be a very reasonable solution to the problem of producing a curve until the work involved in making the necessary calculations is considered, not to mention the mathematical ability required. It was the sort of situation where a little computer help with the calculations was much appreciated. The more complex the profile—imagine an elliptical path, for instance—the more essential computer help became.

Today, thanks to the inclusion of a micro computer as an integral part of even the most basic CNC control systems, the programming of a constant radius curve is a very simple matter indeed, often requiring nothing more than dimensional definition of the target position and the value of the radius. Even the more complex elliptical profiles can be programmed on some control systems simply by defining the major and minor axes.

The reader will recall that the programming of radial cutter paths is referred to as 'circular interpolation', while the facility used to program an elliptical profile is known as a 'canned cycle'.

There is a wide variety of canned cycles currently available with modern machine controllers. A number of these were described in Chapter 1. All of these canned cycles were designed and included in the control system with one objective in mind, that is, to simplify programming.

Canned cycles cater for sequences that are likely to regularly recur. But not all complex profiles regularly recur and when such a profile does occur it can present problems as difficult, and possibly more so, as the problems associated with curves in the early days of NC.

In particular, the machining of complex profiles, or rather the preparation of the part program to achieve the machining, means that fairly complex calculations have to be performed to determine the geometry intersection points. There is also the problem of determining efficient cutter paths to remove stock, and that can also be a laborious business.

It is to meet these requirements that special computer-based programming systems have been developed. The process of using these systems is referred to as Computer Aided Part Programming, generally referred to as CAPP. (Note: the initials CAPP are also used in production engineering to denote Computer Aided Process Planning, which is concerned with the total organisation of a production operation of which Computer Aided Part Programming may be an included activity.)

CAPP provides for a simpler, quicker and more accurate approach to preparing a CNC part program. But at the same time it represents a considerable capital outlay that has to be justified by an eventual increase in efficiency and productivity.

The CAPP process involves preparing a program using a specially developed language, entering the resulting data into a computer and receiving back from the computer a program presented in a format acceptable to the machine controller. During the process the computer will have processed the data to verify its validity and, where necessary, performed computing tasks that would have been mathematically difficult and/or time-consuming if attempted manually.

CAPP can, in the hands of experienced users, provide rapid programming solutions for the most difficult of work. Even for very simple work, where manually prepared programs could be produced fairly quickly, the use of CAPP is still a viable proposition.

A trend among engineering contractors is to ask the potential customer for a drawing of the component that is to be produced and then to program, using CAPP, and then manufacture a component. The result is then returned to the customer with the quotation, indicating very effectively the speed and quality of the service on offer. At the same time the contractor is able to cost the contract precisely, since it will be known exactly how long it took to machine the sample.

A further advantage of CAPP is that the program is prepared and proved 'off-line', that is, away from the machine. Data transfer to the machine is rapid so there is no delay in getting a machine back into production following job changes.

Computer installations

CAPP systems are available for use on all types of computer installations from mainframe to micro.

The large mainframe computers possess the greatest computing power and their use is indispensable for very complex programming requirements.

Unfortunately they are extremely costly and their installation is only economically viable in large organisations where the computing needs—not only for CAPP but for a whole range of industrial and commerical activities—are considerable.

A mainframe computer will cater for a large number of work-stations or terminals which, provided the distance between the two is not excessive, can be permanently cable-linked. Where the distance is considerable they can be linked via the telephone. This also makes it possible to cross international frontiers and even link continents.

Small industrial and commercial organisations can gain access to a mainframe computer, and the required software, on a 'time-share' basis. The computer, which may be many miles distant is accessed via the public telephone network. The facility is available to numerous subscribers and each pays for the actual computing time used; but to this cost it is necessary to add the normal telephone charges which can be considerable.

Subscription to such a system also provides access to a range of back-up services such as the use of the latest software and professional advice regarding its application. Help is also available to solve problems encountered when using the system generally.

In addition, time-share subscribers do not have to conern themselves with maintenance or servicing of the system, as is the case with an in-house installation when a service contract with the manufacturer or supplier would be another costly but essential requirement.

One drawback to time-sharing, assuming that the financial considerations are acceptable, is that access to the computer may not always be conveniently available because too many subscribers are trying to 'log on', or connect into the system, at any one time. Another is that the data security may be inadequate if the work concerned is of a sensitive nature.

Many organisations have requirements that do not justify the installation of a mainframe, but at the same time could not be satisfactorily catered for by time-sharing. They often instal their own large to medium-sized systems. The available capacity and computing power will be less extensive than that available from a mainframe computer, but still capable of servicing a very large organisation.

A feature of these installations is the permanent linking of work stations, or terminals, to the host computer. When terminals are linked in this way they are said to be 'networked'. By this means the complete system may become fully interactive, making it possible for data to be originated and accessed by a number of users. It may be possible for a programmer to utilise data originated by a draughtsperson, thus providing a link between design and manufacture, referred to as CAD/CAM, which is discussed further on page 117. There may also be direct connections to the machine tools on the shop floor, a facility referred to as Direct Numerical Control (DNC). (See page 94.)

A variation of this approach is to transfer the completed part program to a temporary data storage facility on the shop floor, which is situated alongside and connected to the machine that is to manufacture the part. The production controller can download the data into the machine control unit as and when required. Programs can also be downloaded from the machine into the storage unit.

The networking of user terminals described above is also available on even smaller computer installations, but the number of terminals and, of course, the computing power available is proportionally reduced. However, a 'mini' or 'super mini' computer, small enough to fit under a desk, is still capable of handling a fairly comprehensive CAD/CAM system, providing control of both the design and manufacturing elements of engineering and often including other functions such as costing, invoicing, etc.

Finally, there are the installations involving 'micro' or 'super micro' computers. Stand-alone CAPP systems that operate on micro-computers are now capable of handling very complex programming requirements and are widely used. This type of installation is realtively cheap, which makes their installation by smaller companies a feasible proposition.

Micro-based systems can be networked and linked to peripheral equipment such as plotters, printers and tape punches. Provided the distance is not too great, they can also be cable-linked to machine tools.

Because of restrictions on expenditure, most educational establishments have found it necessary to install micro-computer based CAPP systems, and it is this type of installation which students are most likely to use when first being introduced to computer-aided part programming.

Figure 3.1 shows a general arrangement of a CAPP work station utilising a micro-computer.

Figure 3.1 *General arrangement of a CAPP work station.*

It is possible that a company may not become involved in any of the arrangements outlined above, since there are many bureaux or offices which offer a program preparation and proving service. The use of a bureau can sometimes be attractive to companies that do not have sufficient programming work to sustain a part programmer working full time, and which may prefer to retain a lower, and therefore cheaper, level of skill on the shop floor. Even when the skill levels on the shop floor are such that part programming could satisfactorily be undertaken, the use of a bureau, providing an already proved program, means that no time is lost between ending one production run and beginning the next.

The staff of programming bureaux will work in close co-operation with the client company, so that the machining is tackled in a way acceptable to all concerned. In some cases they also offer supporting services associated with the selection of tooling and the design of special work-holding arrangements if required.

Hardware configurations

Whatever the computer installation used, it is possible to establish, in a general way, the hardware configurations associated with CAPP.

The diagram 3.2 shows a very basic computer-aided part programming system: a computer, a data recording facility in the form of a tape punch, a data transfer facility in the form of a tape reader attached to the machine tool and the machine tool itself.

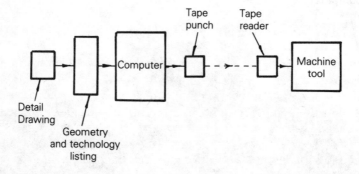

Figure 3.2 *Basic CAPP system.*

In Figure 3.3 this basic arrangement is extended and includes, instead of the tape punch and tape reader, a direct cable link to the machine tool, which is a much quicker and more convenient method of transferring data. When the computer and machine are linked by cable the arrangement is referred to as Direct Numerical Control, DNC.

Figure 3.4 shows the concept extended still further, this time to include cable links to a number of machine tools which may be of different types. These

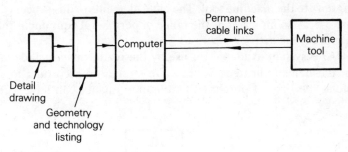

Figure 3.3 *Simple direct numerical control.*

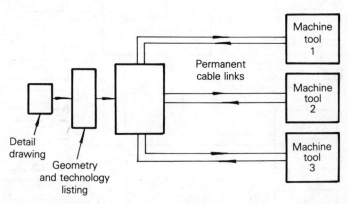

Figure 3.4 *Direct numerical control of a machine group.*

machines may be arranged in a particular way, possibly associated with robot work-handling devices, to form a machining cell.

Taking an even broader view, there may even be a number of programming stations and a number of machines, or machining cells, all linked to the same computer. In this situation the part programming function could be but a small element of a totally integrated computer-controlled manufacturing environment including design, marketing, accounting, materials handling, personnel control and so on. Complex systems such as this are referred to as Computerised Integrated Manufacture, CIM. Of course, the greater the demands on the system the more extensive will be the required computing and data storage facilities.

From the foregoing the reader will appreciate that is is possible for the CAPP system with which he or she is concerned to be a relatively simple stand-alone system, the purpose of which is solely to produce CNC part-programs for a particular machine or a limited number of machines, or it may be an integral part of a much more complex installation.

Even if the overall computing arrangement is complex, it is still possible to consider the CAPP element in isolation and return to the basic objective: preparing a part program with computer assistance and then transferring the resulting data to the machine tool. The main elements in this process are shown in Figure 3.5. Also indicated is the range of peripheral equipment that can be used to support the activity.

The CAPP system available for use by the reader may include all or only some of the items indicated. Systems are structured according to the funds available at the time of purchase, and limited finance can have a restricting effect.

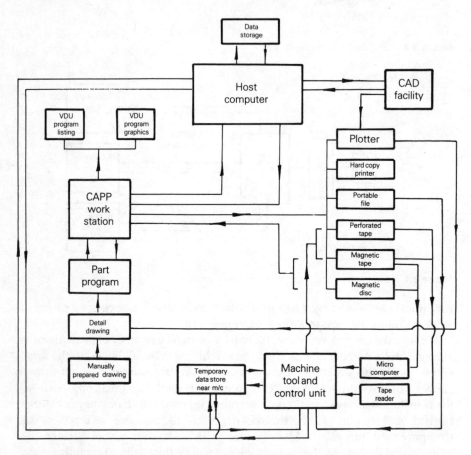

Figure 3.5 *CAPP station incorporated in a system.*

However, it is essential that a part programmer is fully conversant with any system he or she is going to use. Time spent in getting to understand the system before making any attempt to prepare a part program is time well spent, since it can do much to eliminate the time-consuming and often frustrating need to ask for help every time an unfamiliar feature of the system is encountered. Assignment No. 4 included in Chapter 5 is structured in a way that should facilitate the familiarisation process.

Input and control devices

There are a number of ways by which data can be entered into a computer during the CAPP process.

Input via the familiar alpha-numeric keyboard is laborious and rather slow, bearing in mind that the average programmer is likely to be a little lacking in keyboard skills. But since many of the data entries associated with CAPP are repetitive it is possible to speed up the process by using various supplementary devices and techniques.

Selection from a menu, that is a list of options, is one such facility. The menu may be included as an overlay on a digitising tablet or be displayed on the VDU screen.

A digitising tablet is a device like a small rectangular board that is positioned alongside the computer keyboard and is cable-linked to the computer. The tablet is capable of detecting the position of a puck or stylus (see below) when either of these devices is placed upon it.

An overlay is like a plan that divides the surface of the tablet into a number of small areas. Each area is allocated to a specific function such as representing an item from the menu.

A puck is a device with cross-hairs mounted in a small block. It is traversed by hand over the tablet until the cross-hairs are located over the function to be selected. The selection is then confirmed either by an appropriate keystroke or by pressing a button on the puck. A stylus is rather like a pen. It is used to identify the menu item required and the choice is then activated by applying slight pressure.

A digitising tablet is a feature of the programming station illustrated in Figure 3.1, which also shows the puck used for menu selection.

Screen menus can either occupy a complete VDU screen, in which case the graphic image which is an important feature of the CAPP process is temporarily lost, or it can occupy part of the screen so that the graphic image is retained. On small VDUs the second arrangement can mean that the graphic display is rather cramped. A hardware configuration that will eliminate the disadvantages inherent in both arrangements is to have a two-screen display, one for the menu and program listing and one for the graphic display, but this does add to the cost of the installation.

Selection from screen menus can be achieved in several ways. If the menu items are numbered, selection may be via a keyboard input. A second method is to use a light pen which involves directing a light source at the VDU screen which is of a special type known as a 'vector refresh' screen. A variation of this approach is a pen which senses the light being emitted from the screen itself.

Thirdly, the menu items can be selected by moving a cursor—a spot or cross that can be moved about the screen—and then activating the function by making a keystroke or by pressing a button on the cursor control device.

There are a number of devices that are used to control cursor movement. One of the most commonly used is the 'mouse'. It has some resemblance to a real mouse because of its shape and its long tail which is, in fact, the cable connecting it to the computer. Beneath the mouse is a set of wheels; as the mouse is moved about a flat surface alongside the computer—a table top, for instance—the wheels detect the movement and cause the screen cursor to make a corresponding movement.

Another device is the 'tracker ball'. This device has a partially exposed ball mounted in a small box. The ball is rolled around by the palm of the hand. The movement of the ball is detected and, as with the mouse, a corresponding cursor movement appears on the screen.

A third method of cursor control is by the use of a 'joystick'. As this is moved around in all directions the screen cursor moves in unison. A joystick is shown in the illustration of the CAPP work station in Figure 3.6.

It is possible that an area of a digitising tablet can be allocated to represent the VDU screen. The stylus or the puck referred to earlier can then be used to pass over the screen area and effect a corresponding movement on the screen.

Figure 3.6 *Part programming station showing use of computer graphics for program proving.*

Apart from menu selection, a cursor is also used within the CAPP process to identify geometric elements such as points, lines and circles that have been constructed on the screen. For example, to construct a line at 90° to a base line will first need a menu selection to identify the type of construction required, followed by identification of the point on the base line at which the second line is to be constructed. The cursor will be moved to identify the point, and the function activated by making a keystroke or pressing a button on the cursor control device. Similarly, a line may need to be deleted, in which case it is first identified by positioning the cursor and then removed by making a keystroke or by pressing a delete button on the cursor control.

The foregoing description has, of necessity, been general in nature. Cursor controllers, even of one particular type, are very variable in design. The way in which cursors are used varies from one CAPP system to another. The essential thing to appreciate is that a part programmer is not required to be familiar with all the possibilities; nevertheless it will be necessary to become competent in the application of the particular devices associated with the program system he or she will be using, and this can only be achieved by using the equipment.

Computer assisted programming activities

In Chapter 2 the procedure for manual part programming, taking the detail drawing as a starting point, was listed. That list is reproduced below, but this time the programming activities that will be assisted by the use of CAPP are shown in heavy type.

1. Select a machine capable of handling the required work.
2. Prepare a schedule of machining operations.
3. Determine work holding and location techniques.
4. Determine tooling requirements and their identity.
5. Document, or otherwise record, instructions relating to work holding, work location and tooling.
6. **Calculate suitable cutting speeds and feed rates.**
7. **Calculate profile intersecting points, arc centres etc.**
8. **Determine appropriate tool paths including the use of canned cycles and sub-routines.**
9. **Prepare the part program.**
10. **Prove the part program and edit as necessary.**
11. **Record the part program for future use.**

Before proceeding further it is necessary to make the point that the more practical elements of the list, that is, those numbered from 1 to 5, are as necessary for CAPP as they are for manual part programming. CAPP does not eliminate the need for the programmer to have a good grounding in the practicalities of metal cutting. The reader is referred to the fuller consideration given to these aspects of CNC machining which is included in Chapter 2.

To return to the CAPP process. It will be assumed that consideration has been duly given to the practicalities of a particular machining task, and the computer-aided element of preparing the part program can begin.

It is not possible to precisely list the stages in the CAPP process since there is some variation in approach according to the type of system being used. But in general terms the stages may be itemised as follows:

1. Define the geometric detail of the component. This will involve a series of individually constructed elements that embraces the final component detail.
2. Use the geometric detail to define appropriate machining sequences.
3. Supplement the proposed machining sequences with technology data relating to tooling, feed rates, spindle speeds etc.
4. Process these data to determine tool paths and to produce a cutter location data file.
5. Post-process these data into a form or language that is acceptable to the machine to be used.
6. Transmit these data direct to the machine tool. Alternatively, a punched tape may be produced, or the program otherwise recorded for future use.

CAPP systems

Before a CAPP system can be used to prepare a program, time will have to be spent in becoming familiar with the techniques or language to be used—just as it is necessary to study the language of a machine control system before programs for a particular machine can be prepared manually. But the use of CAPP does have a major advantage in this respect: it is probable that the programmer will be required to become familiar with only one technique, since it is possible to post-process or translate the data into whatever machine control language is to be used.

It is not possible in a text of this nature to give a comprehensive review of every CAPP system since there are far too many currently in use. Neither would it be of value to consider a particular system in detail. Later in the text, however, programming examples are included in an attempt to give at least a general impression of some of the variations that exist.

In reality, a part programmer will find it necessary to devote as much time as possible to becoming proficient in the application of the particular system he or she will be required to use. Some of the techniques and skills developed in the use of one system are likely to be transferable to another if the need arises.

Although the number of CAPP systems available are many and varied they may be generally defined as being either (i) language, or (ii) graphics based.

The basic difference between the two concepts is the way in which the appropriate tool paths for the machining sequences are ascertained. The following text deals with language-based programming. Graphics-based programming is discussed further on page 115.

Language-based systems

Early CAPP systems were entirely language-based, the geometry of the part being described by a series of statements constructed from letters of the alphabet, numbers and a few other symbols. The systems were not interactive, there was no indication if errors had been made in the data, and therefore no correction was possible during the input process. Confirmation of the validity of data could only be ascertained by processing it. If necessary the program could then be edited. The only visual confirmation of the program data was via a diagram produced on an interfaced plotter after the data entry was completed.

Modern language-based CAPP systems also use alpha-numeric input supplemented by certain symbols, but have been considerably improved by the incorporation of computer graphics. As data is entered there is an instant corresponding graphic display giving an indication of the validity of the input. The systems are fully interactive: if data is not acceptable the fact will be indicated, often with messages to indicate why this is so, and the programmer can then act on this information and modify the input as programming proceeds.

Having defined the component by the use of a series of geometric statements the programmer then selects elements from the overall construction and includes these in what is, in effect, a composite statement that will form the basis of a particular machining operation. The composite statement, which may represent, for example, a profile or a series of holes, will be expressed in language form.

The composite statements are now supplemented by data relating to speeds and feeds, tooling etc. These are referred to as 'technology statements', and are discussed further on page 111.

At this stage these data are processed to determine tool paths and to generate a cutter location data file, referred to as CL Data. Finally, the data are post-processed to generate a program in machine tool code for the particular machine to be used. Each of these stages is explained further in the following text.

Geometric definition

It is assumed that a person making a study of CAPP will already be familiar with manual part programming techniques, and will therefore appreciate that any machined feature or profile can be geometrically defined. He or she will already be familiar with defining tool movements in relation to the workpiece as being linear, circular and point-to-point. An appreciation of how one geometric feature can intersect with another and the need to dimensionally define such intersection points should also be well understood.

In manual part programming the profile is, in effect, split up into its geometric elements. This is also the case with CAPP, in which the shape or feature to be machined is expressed in terms of directions, distances, lines, points and circles.

The way in which these geometric elements are generally defined when using CAPP systems is listed below. The lists should not be considered to be definitive since the approach to geometric construction differs between programming systems, and there are also variations in the words used to describe what is essentially the same feature. A further complication is that some of the definitions used, while perfectly logical and therefore acceptable when applied to geometric construction involving computer graphics, do not conform to true mathematical expression. However, the reader is assured that the descriptions that follow are typical of those likely to be encountered.

Directions are defined in the usual way, that is by the use of the letters X, Y and Z which relate to the axes of movement of the machine tools. Distances are given a dimensional value in millimetres or inches and angles are stated in degrees.

A point may be defined in a number of ways as follows:

(a) As a zero;
(b) as a point with known Cartesian co-ordinates;
(c) as a point with known polar co-ordinates;
(d) as an intersection of two straight lines;
(e) as an intersection of a straight line and a curve;
(f) as an intersection of two curves.

Examples of the above definitions are illustrated in Figures 3.7 (a) to (f) respectively.

Straight lines may also be defined in a number of ways and the following descriptions correspond to the illustrations in Figures 3.8 (a) to (h).

(a) As being parallel to a stated axis;
(b) as being at a known distance from a previously defined point and at a known angle to a previously defined straight line;
(c) as being between two known points;
(d) as being tangential to two known circles;
(e) as being parallel to a defined straight line;
(f) as being perpendicular to a defined straight line;
(g) as being perpendicular to a defined point;
(h) as passing through a defined point.

Circles may be defined as follows, and as illustrated in Figures 3.9 (a) to (g).

(a) As a radius passing through two defined points;
(b) as a radius passing through three defined points;
(c) as a centre point and passing through a defined point;
(d) as a centre point and tangential to a defined straight line;
(e) as being tangential to a defined line, passing through a defined point and with a known radius;

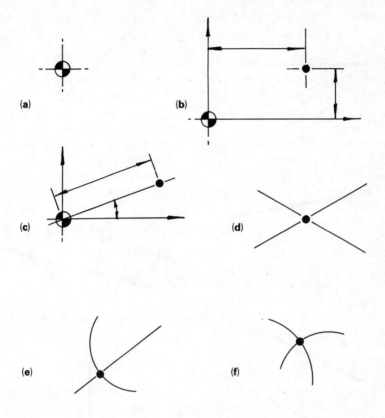

Figure 3.7 *Point definition.*

(f) as being tangential to two defined lines and with a known radius;
(g) as being tangential to three lines and with a known radius.

A further complication with some constructions is that two versions are sometimes possible. Consider Figure 3.10(a), a radius passing through two defined points. One construction is shown in full line and an alternative construction is shown in broken line. Similarly, the construction shown in Figure 3.10(b), of a circle of given radius tangential to two defined lines, has two possible versions as indicated.

Clearly there is a need to clarify the situation by providing the new element with a sense of orientation or direction in relation to the existing geometry. The way this is achieved differs between one system and another and the student will require specific instructions relating to the system he or she will be using.

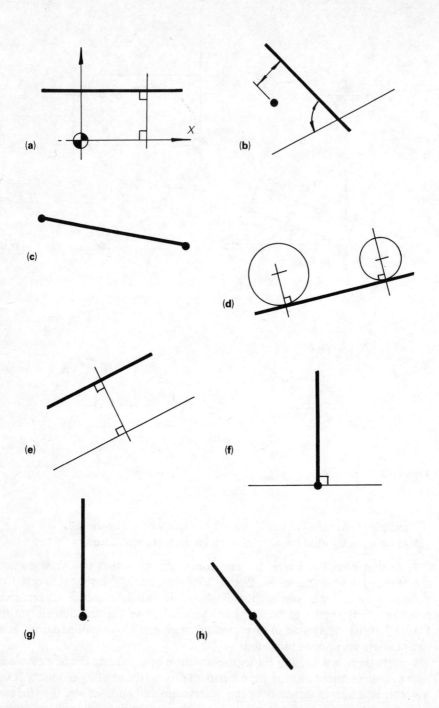

Figure 3.8 *Line definition.*

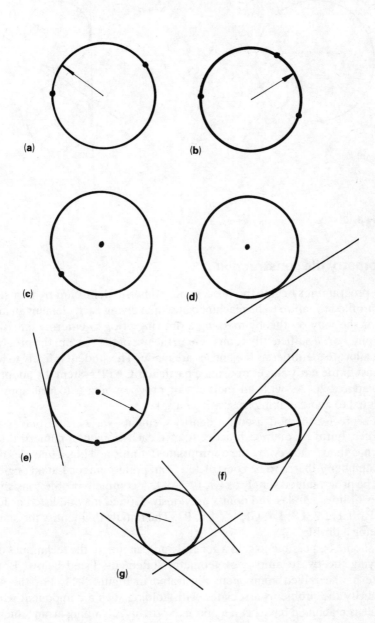

Figure 3.9 *Circle definition.*

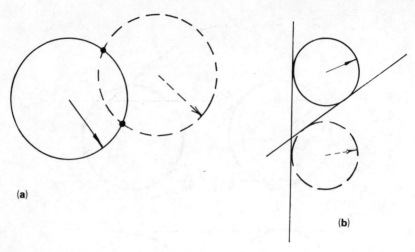

(a)

(b)

Figure 3.10 *Alternative constructions.*

Geometry file construction

The programmer begins the process of geometric definition by first studying the profile or feature to be machined and then giving each element an identity. He or she may do this by marking a drawing prior to entering data into the computer or, if sufficiently competent in the use of the system, the programmer may allocate identities as the entries are made. The student is likely to benefit, at least in the early stages of using a particular CAPP system, by adopting the first approach. As with all methods of programming a logical approach is essential to avoid making frustrating mistakes.

The precise method used to identify elements varies from one system to another, but it is common practice to give each element a numerical identity which is then followed by the appropriate definition. Thus a line identified as line number 7 that is to be constructed from point number 1 at an angle of 90° may be programmed simply as L7, P1, A90. A complete profile consisting of a series of lines, circles and points previously defined may be listed as follows: PF, P1, L1, L2, L3, L4, C1, L5, L6, P2. The initials PF identify the statement as being a profile.

It should be possible to gain a general appreciation of the techniques used by studying the two examples of geometry statements listed below. Both lists relate to the milled component illustrated in Figure 3.11. For the sake of simplicity the problems associated with holding such a component while the profile is machined have been ignored. Normally, clamping arrangements and work-holding devices have to be accommodated within the part program if collisions are to be avoided. Areas they will occupy, which in effect become 'no go' areas for the tool, have to be dimensionally identified and may be displayed graphically as part of the general geometry.

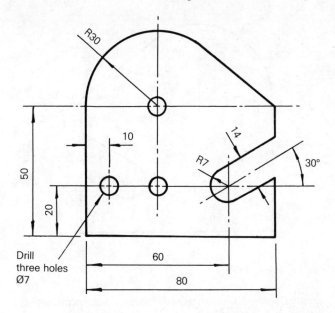

Material: mild steel 10 mm thick.

Figure 3.11 *Component detail.*

The lists which follow were prepared by two different people and their preparation involved the use of two different CAPP systems. The result is two different approaches to the geometry definition. Reference to Figures 3.12 and 3.13 will indicate how each person chose to define the geometry.

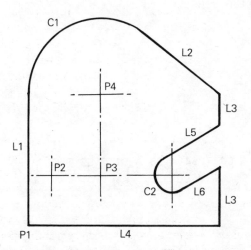

Figure 3.12 *Profile definition - CADMASS.*

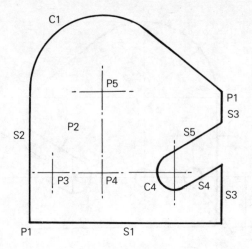

Figure 3.13 *Profile definition - PEPS.*

The reader will note the common use of P to indicate a point and C to indicate a circle. But there, apart from the numerical identity referred to above, the similarities end. Even a basic feature such as a straight line is defined on one system using the letter L and on the other system using the letter S. Further study of the lists will show that the variations become even more pronounced when the individual elements are gathered together to define a profile.

Example No. 1 Software: PEPS

```
PART EXAMPLE 1
WIN X-5 Y-5 Z0 X100 Y100 Z0
S1=H 0
S2=V 0
S3=V80
C1=X30 Y50 30
C4=X60 Y20 7
S4=B30 AC4
S5=B30 TC4
P1=X80 Y50
S6=TC1  P1
P3=X10 Y20
P4=X30 Y20
P5=C1
K1 P1 A S3 A S5 A C4 T S4 A S3 A S1 T S2 T C1 A S6  P1 EK
```

Example No. 2 Software: CADMASS

```
PART-PROGRAM: 1
================
10  SYS,XPL-60,YPL-60,AXES,SCA1.5
20  C1,X30,Y50,R-30
30  L1,C1,A90
40  L10,X,Y50,A0
50  L3,-LY,X80
60  P10,L10,L3
70  L2,C1,P10
80  L4,-LX,Y
90  C2,X60,Y20,R7
100 L5,C2,A-150
110 L6,C2,A30
120 P20,X-10,Y-10
130 P1,X,Y
140 PF1,P1,L1,C1,L2,L3,L5,C2,L6,L3,L4,P1
150 P2,X10,Y20
160 P3,X30,Y20
170 P4,C1
180 SET1,SUM,P2,TO,P4
```

Two further examples of the geometry statements used with each of the above systems are given below. In this instance they relate to the turned component illustrated in Figure 3.14. An interesting exercise which the reader may care to undertake is to identify, on the drawing, the geometric elements as listed.

The CADMASS program also includes the technology statements to which reference will be made later.

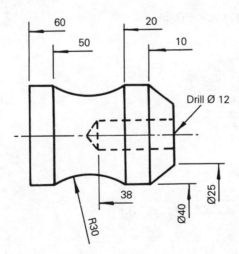

Figure 3.14 *Component detail.*

Example No. 3 Software: PEPS

```
WIN Z-5 X-100 Z80 X100
S1 V0
S2 V60
S3 20 LS2
S4 10 LS2
S5 50 LS2
S6 H40
P1= S5   S6
P2= S6   S3
C1=L P1   P2 30
P3=60 0
P4=0 0
P5=60 12.5
P6= S4   S6
S7= P5   P6
K1   P3 T S2 T S7 A S6
P2
T C1
P1
A S6
A S1
P4 EK
COPY K1 K2
MIR X0 K2
ERA
DRA K1 K2
```

Example No. 4 Software: CADMASS

```
10  SYS,ZPL100,XPL-75,SCA3
20  SYS,AXES
30  P1,Z3,X
40  L1,-LZ,X
50  L2,LX,Z
60  L3,Z,X25,Z-10,X40
70  L4,-LZ,X40
80  P3,Z-20,X40
90  P4,Z-50,X40
100 C1,P3,P4,R-30
110 L5,-LZ,X40
120 L6,LX,Z-63
130 L7,P1,A90
140 L8,-LZ,X50
150 P2,L6,L8
160 PFR,P1,L7,L8,P2
170 PFF,P1,L1,L2,L3,L4,C1,I,L5,L6,P2
180 CLS
190 SYS,AXES
200 PLOT,PFR
210 PLOT,PFF
220 CTUR,X200,Z100
```

Geometry data

```
230 TOOL1,CODE1,FA1,CS200,FR.35,DP2.5
240 OVC.5,L1,L6
250 RUGV,LZ,0
260 RUGH
270 TOOL2,CODE1,FA2,CS200,FR.25,DP1,HA45
280 RUGH
290 TOOL3,CODE2,FA3,CS250,FR.1
300 CLS
310 SYS,AXES
320 FINI,L1,L6
330 TOOL4,CODE5,FA4,CS25,FR.15,D10
340 DRIL,Z3,LENG38
350 ID, READING - TURNING DEMO 1/7/86
360 END
```

Technology data

Verification of geometry statements

Most language-based systems are fully interactive: the correctness of data input is verified as programming proceeds and error messages are displayed if appropriate. This ensures that the data input is acceptable to the system, but it does not necessarily ensure that the programmer has not made other mistakes, so it makes sense to re-process the input in its entirety as a final check.

When the geometry statements have been verified as being correct it is possible to obtain a print from an interfaced printer of the data listing. This may be required for filing for future reference, forming part of the general documentation relating to that particular job.

It is also possible to obtain printed copies of the graphic construction developed during the programming process. Figures 3.15 and 3.16 illustrate the graphics that appeared on the VDU screen when, using the PEPS software, the geometry statements were entered for the milling exercise in Figure 3.11 and the turning exercise in Figure 3.14 respectively. The shapes of the two components can readily be identified as the boundary of each part is indicated by a full line while the construction lines are indicated by the use of a broken line.

Technology statements

After the geometry of the component has been defined the programmer has to consider the more practical aspects of producing a machined component, such as the sequence of operations, the cutting tools to be used and the choice of appropriate cutting speeds and feeds. If the programming task has been approached in a logical manner most of these aspects will have been considered before the CAPP process was started. Now data defining these factors has to be added to the part program to supplement the geometric data previously entered. It is possible that some computer assistance may be available.

Technology statements are included in the CADMASS'program|above|.

When defining the sequence and types of machining operations to be carried out the programmer will be required to take into consideration the special

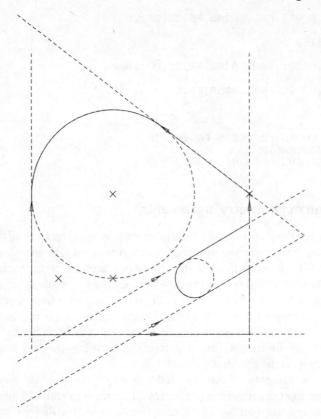

Figure 3.15 *Geometric construction on a milled component - PEPS software.*

cycles that are an inbuilt feature of the programming system. All the normal machining sequences—drilling, screw cutting, face milling, boring etc—are likely to be catered for. It will also be possible to generate sub-routines. To use these facilities effectively the programmer will need to be fully conversant with the particular system being used, and this is only achieved by experience.

It is likely that the tooling available for a particular machine will be listed and contained on file within the programming system. Such a data file is referred to as a 'tool library' and can be displayed on the screen. All the data relevant to a particular tool, such as the material from which it is made, its shape and dimensions, will be indicated together with an identity code for use within the part program. The dimensions of the tool, in particular its radius or diameter, are of particular importance since they will have a direct effect on the cutter paths automatically generated at the next stage of the CAPP process.

Cutting speeds and feeds can be determined without computer assistance, and entered into the program in much the same way as when preparing a normal CNC part program. On the other hand there may be assistance via the system in response to data input identifying the cutting tool and the part

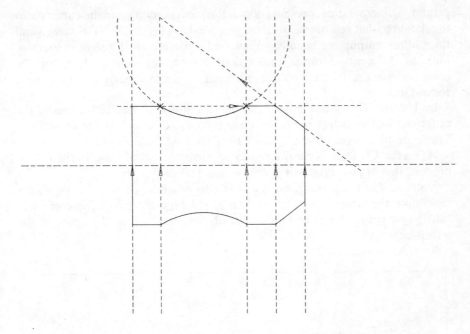

Figure 3.16 *Geometric construction of turned component - PEPS software.*

material. The correct speeds and feeds will then be automatically determined and included in the program. (The reader may recall from Chapter 1 that such a facility is available on some conversational MDI systems.)

Cutter location data

When the computer is programmed with all the data defining the part geometry, the machining sequence, tooling etc., the process of determining the cutter location data, referred to as the CL Data, can begin. In simple terms, the CL Data can be described as the dimensional definition of the cutter path from a defined datum point.

In determining the CL Data the computer automatically calculates the movements necessary to achieve the geometric features previously defined. In doing so, account will be taken of cutter sizes; where appropriate, compensation for the cutter radius will be made. Where area clearance is required, and excess stock material has to be removed, the computer will determine the appropriate tool paths.

CL Data can be viewed on the VDU screen and a printout can be obtained if required.

Tool paths can be displayed graphically, in some cases with a three-dimensional or pictorial effect. It is also possible to produce, via a plotter or a printer, a diagramatic representation of the part geometry and the cutter paths in relation to that geometry. Both the graphical display on the VDU screen and the plotter output are usually enhanced by the use of different colours to indicate different features: one colour for the geometric shape of the component and a different colour indicating the paths of each tool to be used, for instance.

In Figure 3.17 and Figure 3.18 the printouts of the cutter paths for programming the components shown in Figures 3.11 and 3.14 are illustrated. These printouts were obtained when using the CADMASS system.

When the CL Data is considered to be correct the final stage in the CAPP process, that of post-processing, can be undertaken.

With the CL Data file compiled it is also possible, on some systems, to determine the time that will be taken to machine the part. The computer calculation is based on the cutting speeds and feeds entered as part of the technology data.

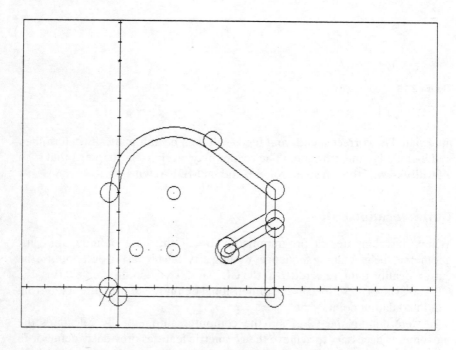

Figure 3.17 *Plotted cutter paths for milled component - CADMASS software.*

Post-processing

Post-processing is the stage in the CAPP process where the CL Data and other information relevant to the machining of the component is assembled into a form that will be accepted and meaningful to the control system of the

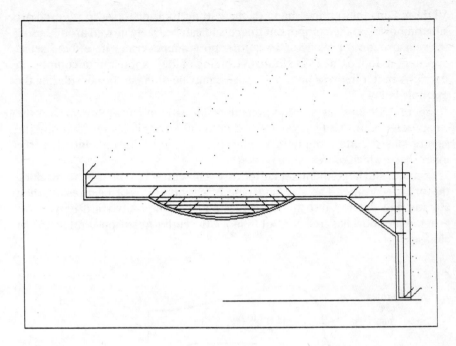

Figure 3.18 *Plotted cutter paths for turned component - CADMASS software.*

particular machine to be used. Features such as G and M codes, previously not part of the program data, are now automatically incorporated.

Because there are many variations in the control systems fitted to machine tools it is necessary to have a post-processor to suit each control system for which part programs are to be prepared. The manufacturers of CAPP systems will supply specific post-processors to order, these being immediately available for the more widely-used machine controls. It is also possible with some systems to purchase a 'writing kit' which permits users to compile their own post-processor for it is actually a relatively simple computer program. In this way, if a new machine is acquired it can be readily assimilated into the CAPP system.

The post-processing of data into a machine control language is achieved very rapidly, being simply a case of making a few key strokes. The resulting program can now be recorded for future use in whatever form is deemed to be appropriate.

Graphics-based systems

Graphics-based systems are referred to as Graphical Numerical Control (GNC). They differ from language-based systems in the following manner.

When the geometric detail of the component has been constructed on the

VDU screen, the outline shape of the cutting tool, or tools, to be used are superimposed on the component image and can be freely moved around using the cursor control device. Thus the programmer can, in effect, select appropriate tool paths to facilitate machining of the component or component detail. A better impression of the process may be obtained by considering the example below.

Figure 3.19 illustrates a component detail as it might be 'drawn' on the computer screen. Also shown are two different-sized circles representing the superimposed cutters required to machine the outside profile and clear the inner shape which represents a pocket.

Consider the large-diameter cutter first. This cutter is to be used to machine the outside profile. The size and type of cutter will have been established already and entered into the data file, possibly via a keyboard entry. The programmer now has free control to move the cutter to any position he or she chooses.

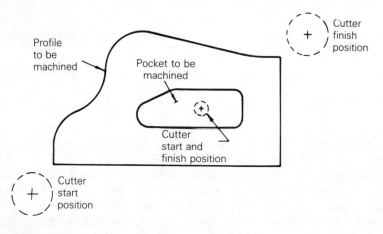

Figure 3.19 *A graphical numerical control display.*

The cutter is first positioned in a suitable starting position. If cutter radius compensation is required then the starting position will be a suitable distance away from the profile so that the cutter can attain the correct position before contacting the work surface. This start position is then entered into the data file either via the cursor control or the keyboard.

Having established the start position the programmer moves the cutter image to the finish position and this too is entered into the file.

Using this very simple data entry the computer is able to compute the complete cutter route, indicating it on the screen alongside the component. It will also list, in numerical form, the cutter location in relation to a previously established datum at each stage in the machining process; the list appears on a second VDU or an interfaced printer.

Now consider the machining of the pocket. To achieve this the programmer simply has to move the cutter to the start position at the centre of the pocket as indicated. All that is now required are keyboard data entries to establish that a pocket clearance routine is required. From this data entry the computer will establish all the moves necessary to clear the pocket and machine the final profile. Again, the cutter paths will be shown graphically and also presented in numerical form, the dimensional values being in relation to a predetermined datum.

Note that in this simple description no mention has been made of movement in the third, that is, Z axis. Clearance in the Z axis, and the depth to which the cutter is required to go, will be entered via the keyboard as the program is constructed. Data relating to speeds and feeds will be entered in the same way.

In addition to the component image displayed on the screen, it is possible to include any work-holding or tool-holding arrangements that may influence the choice of tool paths. An example of such a display for a turning operation is shown in Figure 3.6. By including such detail it is possible for the programmer to be reasonably confident that all programmed moves will be collision-free.

As with language-based systems it will be possible to obtain copies of the data entered via an interfaced printer.

Data can also be re-processed to verify its accuracy prior to post-processing into machine control language.

The CAD/CAM link

The use of computers as an aid to manufacturing processes is referred to as Computer Aided Manufacture (CAM). The CAPP process is part of that general definition.

The use of computers to facilitate drafting or design work is referred to as Computer Aided Drafting/Design (CAD).

Together CAD and CAM form the basis of Computer Aided Engineering (CAE).

From the foregoing text the reader will now appreciate that an important element of the CAPP process is the geometric definition of the component detail. It is, of course, also central to any computer-aided drafting process. It is logical therefore that the two processes should be linked. Most CAD/CAM software currently in use provides this facility.

The transfer involves reducing the detail drawing to its basic geometry by removing all dimensions, notes, leader lines etc. This is easily and instantly achieved as the drawing will have been compiled by the use of overlays or layers, with one layer containing the basic drawing and subsequent layers containing dimensions and other data. Each layer is capable of being displayed independently of the others.

With the drawing reduced to its basic form the geometry created as part of the drafting process can be used for part programming purposes, thus eliminating the geometry construction stage of the CAPP process, and speeding part programming activity considerably.

Questions

1 List the advantages of computer aided part programming when compared with manual part programming.

2 List and briefly describe the main stages in the CAPP process.

3 Make a block diagram to illustrate a basic 'stand-alone' CAPP system.

4 Explain what is meant by 'time-sharing' and list the advantages and disadvantages of using such a facility.

5 Describe three methods that may be used for menu selection from a digitising tablet.

6 Describe three methods of cursor control that may be used to identify graphic features on a VDU screen.

7 Describe three general methods for geometrically defining a point, a straight line and a circle or curve.

8 List the various data that would be included as technology statements during the preparation of a part program.

9 Explain what is meant by 'cutter location data'.

10 Explain the function of 'post-processing' and state how a range of machines having a variety of control systems would be accommodated.

4

PART PROGRAMMING CALCULATIONS

Having read the previous chapters the reader should now be aware that the application of CNC technology to the production of machined parts requires considerable knowledge and ability.

In the first instance there is the practical expertise associated with process planning, work-holding, tooling and so on. In this respect there is continuity between what was expected of the traditional machine shop craftsman and what is required of the machine shop technician involved with new technology. The advent of CNC has had a considerable effect on the way machining tasks are tackled, but the need for practical expertise remains much the same. Further, this expertise can only be obtained by shop floor experience. It is assumed that students involved with CNC part programming will have acquired, or will be in the process of acquiring, this essential knowledge.

Secondly, the machine shop technician using modern technology is required to become familiar with the programming languages employed by the control units fitted to the machines he or she will be using. In addition, if computer aided part programming facilities are to be used then the technician must also become proficient in the application of these techniques. In the last few years those who have been involved in the education and training of others in the use of CNC technology have found that students, in general, rapidly master the use of programming systems. The most advanced aspect of the technology seems to be the one which is most quickly mastered and applied, but unfortunately its application is often marred by a lack of practical expertise and mathematical ability.

It is the mathematical ability of workshop technicians that is the third area of expertise that has to be considered. Mention was made earlier of the need for the part programmer to be able to carry out calculations associated with speeds and feeds, profile intersection points, arc centres and so on. Competent manual part programming is not possible without a fairly well-developed mathematical ability and a sound understanding of geometric construction.

The mathematics involved in part programming are essentially practical in nature. It is assumed that readers of this text will have already developed these particular skills, and that they will be capable of carrying out the necessary calculations.

Thus it is not the purpose here to provide a text for the student who wishes to learn mathematical concepts, but rather to provide a means of revising certain areas that are of particular interest to the CNC part programmer, and to supply the student with examples which will develop the ability to deal with the mathematical elements of programming tasks. Reference to the geometry data contained below may be helpful in some cases.

While the following exercises are intended primarily for manual solution, a number of them will serve to introduce the facilities afforded by computer aided part programming before the student attempts more comprehensive problems.

Geometry data

The following information is provided for reference purposes.

Pythagoras' Theorem

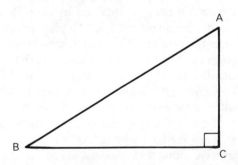

$$AB^2 = AC^2 + BC^2$$
$$AB = \sqrt{AC^2 + BC^2}$$

Similarly,

$$AC = \sqrt{AB^2 - BC^2} \quad \text{and} \quad BC = \sqrt{AB^2 - AC^2}$$

Example Figure 4.1 shows the detail of a milled component which has been dimensioned without regard to part programming needs. Dimension X is required. Using Pythagoras' Theorem, calculate its value.

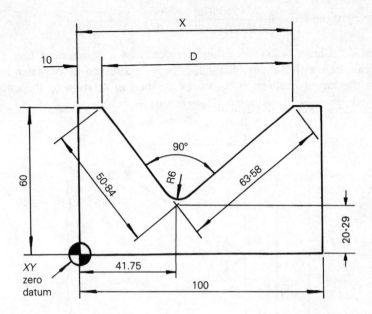

Figure 4.1 *Using Pythagoras Theorem.*

$$D^2 = 50.84^2 + 63.58^2$$
$$D = {}^2\sqrt{50.84^2 + 63.58^2}$$
$$= {}^2\sqrt{6627.2}$$
$$= 81.41$$
$$X = 81.41 + 10 = 91.41$$

Trigonometrical ratios

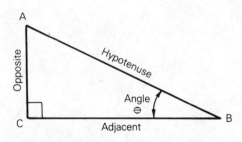

Sine of the angle $\theta = \dfrac{\text{Opposite}}{\text{Hypotenuse}} = \dfrac{\text{AC}}{\text{AB}}$

Cosine of the angle $\theta = \dfrac{\text{Adjacent}}{\text{Hypotenuse}} = \dfrac{\text{BC}}{\text{AB}}$

Tangent of the angle $\theta = \dfrac{\text{Opposite}}{\text{Adjacent}} = \dfrac{AC}{BC}$

Example Figure 4.2 shows the part detail of a component that is to be programmed with dimensional values being expressed in incremental mode. Thus the target position B has to be defined in relation to the end of the previous move A. Calculate the dimensions X and Y.

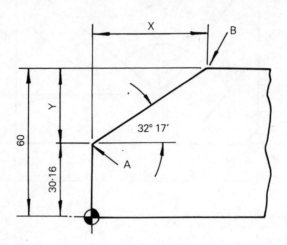

Figure 4.2 *Using trigonometrical ratios.*

To calculate Y

$Y = 60 - 30.16 = 29.84$

To calculate X:

$$\text{Tan } 32°17' = \frac{\text{OPP}}{\text{ADJ}} = \frac{Y}{X}$$

$$X = \frac{Y}{\text{Tan } 32°17'}$$

$$= \frac{29.84}{0.6317}$$

$$= 47.23$$

The sine rule

For use with triangles that are not right-angled.

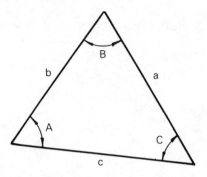

$$\frac{a}{\sin A} = \frac{b}{\sin B} = \frac{c}{\sin C}$$

Example Figure 4.3 shows a drawing detail of a machined feature. To facilitate part programming, calculate the dimensions X and Y.

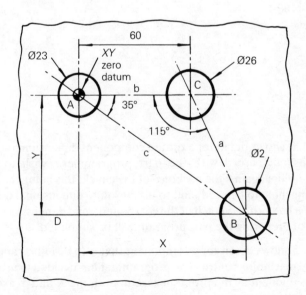

Figure 4.3 *Using the sine rule.*

To calculate the dimensions X and Y it is first necessary to determine $A\hat{B}D$ and the length AB from the information given. Note that AB = c.

$A\hat{B}D = B\hat{A}C = 35°$

$A\hat{C}B = 180 - (115 + 35) = 30°$

Using the Sine Rule to calculate AB:

$$\frac{b}{Sin\ B} = \frac{c}{Sin\ C}$$

$$\frac{b \times Sin\ C}{Sin\ B} = c$$

$$c = \frac{60 \times Sin\ 115°}{Sin\ 30°}$$

$$= \frac{60 \times 0.906}{0.5}$$

$$= 108.72$$

To calculate dimensions X and Y using trigonometry:

$$Cos\ 35° = \frac{ADJ}{HYP} = \frac{X}{AB}$$

$$Cos\ 35° \times AB = X$$

$$X = 0.819 \times 108.72$$

$$= 89.042$$

$$Sin\ 35° = \frac{OPP}{ADJ} = \frac{Y}{AB}$$

$$Sin\ 35° \times AB = Y$$

$$Y = .574 \times 108.72$$

$$Y = 62.405$$

Exercises

1. Figure 4.4. shows details of a turned component dimensioned in a manner that does not accord with the part programmer's wish to locate the prepared billet against the backface of the chuck, this being the Z axis zero for the machine to be used, and to use absolute dimensional definition.

    Make a half profile sketch of the component, and dimension it so that the process of preparing the part program will be simplified.

2. Figure 4.5 shows details of a component that is to be milled and drilled on a vertical machining centre. The programmer has decided to use the corner of the component as the program zero in both the X and Y axes. Make a sketch of the component and dimension it in a manner which will be more convenient from a programming point of view, assuming that the programmer intends to use incremental positioning data.

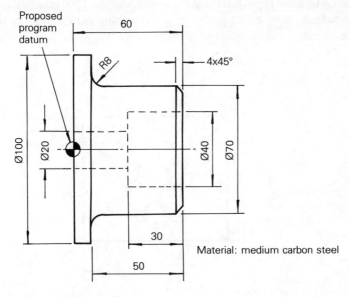

Figure 4.4

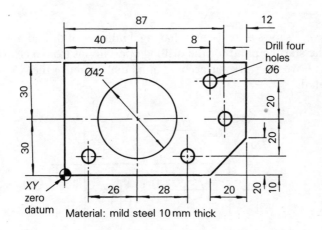

Figure 4.5

3. There is no obvious sequence in which to program the drilling of the six holes in the component shown in Figure 4.6. The programmer has initially chosen to adopt the sequence ABCDEF as indicated on the drawing. Since the time taken to actually drill the holes will be the same whatever sequence is used, the only time saving that can be made is by using the shortest possible positioning route.

Using graph paper, draw the component accurately to scale, and check by measuring whether the proposed route is in fact the most efficient. If it proves not to be the shortest possible, state an alternative.

Given that the rapid feed rate for the machine is 2500 mm/min, estimate the total time saving that could be made by using this different positioning route, during a production run of 5000 components.

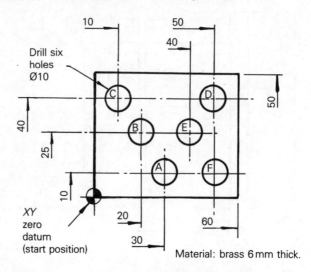

Figure 4.6

4. Figure 4.7 shows a component having a number of drilled holes. Assume that the starting point for the drilling operation is from a clearance plane 4 mm above the work surface and immediately above the XY zero datum indicated.

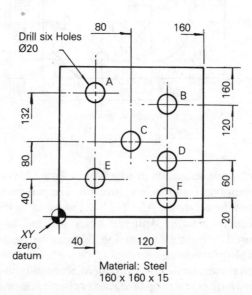

Figure 4.7

Accurately redraw the component on graph paper, and by scaling the drawing determine the most economical drilling sequence, taking account of the time taken in positioning.

5. The milled impression shown in Figure 4.8 is to be machined on a vertical machining centre.

   Determine the shortest continuous tool path possible to machine the impression, assuming a start and finish position at zero in the X and Y axes. (Ignore movement in the Z axis as this is likely to be identical regardless of the route chosen in the X and Y axes.)

   Calculate the time taken to complete the operation given that the rapid traverse rate for the machine is 4000 mm/min, the feed rate for the metal cutting operation is 0.3 mm/rev, the spindle speed is 3000 rev/min and the Z up position is 200 mm from the Z axis zero which is set at 2 mm above the top face of the work. Assume the tool change position is immediately above the XY axes zero.

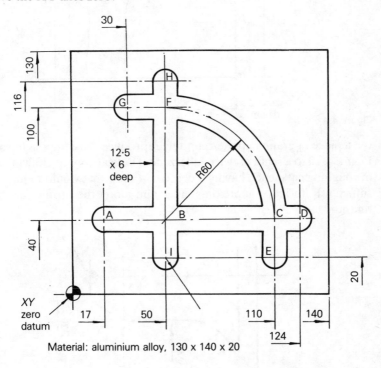

Material: aluminium alloy, 130 × 140 × 20

Figure 4.8

6. Assume that the feature shown in Figure 4.9, the machining of which involves a certain amount of stock removal prior to a finishing pass along the profile, is to be produced on a machine with a control system which does not possess a suitable canned cycle. Thus the programmer has no

alternative but to determine, manually, the most efficient way of clearing the step. He or she may choose to program a series of cuts, with a small amount of cutter overlap to ensure a clean face, with the bulk of the stock being removed as the cutter travels along the X axis or, alternatively, along the Y axis.

Reproduce the pocket accurately to scale on graph paper and determine which, if any, of the two cutting directions would remove the stock in the shortest time. Assume a cutter diameter of 12 mm.

Express the movements required to remove the stock in terms of X and Y values which could be incorporated as data in a part program.

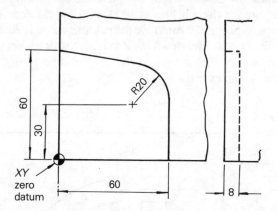

Figure 4.9

7. On a piece of graph paper, accurately reproduce the component shown in Figure 4.10 to a scale of twice full size and indicate on the drawing a series of roughing cuts, each having a depth of 4 mm, that would reduce the bar sufficiently to leave approximately 1 mm along the profile for the final finishing cut.

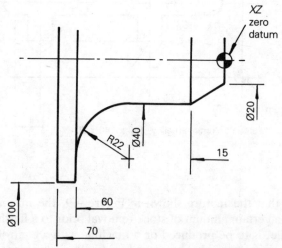

Figure 4.10

Express the roughing cuts in terms of X and Z, that would enable them to be incorporated in the part program.

8. The angular feature of the component shown in Figure 4.11 is to be machined on a tape-controlled machine, the control system of which does not include the cutter radius compensation facility. Calculate the incremental linear moves that will need to be included in the part program, assuming movement starts from and returns to the indicated datum. The diameter of the cutter to be used is 50 mm, and there is to be approach and overrun distances of 4 mm as indicated.

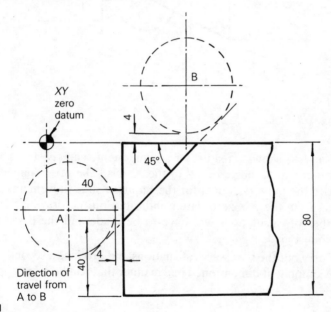

Figure 4.11

9. Calculate the incremental linear movements in the X and Z axes that will be required to finish machine the taper shown in Figure 4.12.

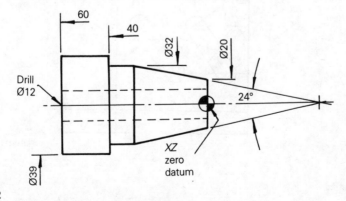

Figure 4.12

10. Figure 4.13 shows a feature of a turned component. Two of the dimensions necessary to complete a part program are not given.
Determine which dimensions are missing and calculate their values.

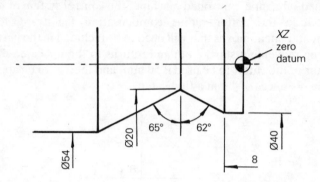

Figure 4.13

11. Figure 4.14 shows a feature of a component, namely, two parallel slots positioned at an angle of 52° to the X axis. The programmer intends to specify the numerical data for the required slide movements in absolute terms from the XY zero datum indicated on the drawing. To do this a number of calculations will have to be made and the drawing must be redimensioned.

Carry out the necessary calculations and produce a second drawing of the component dimensioned in a manner that will be more appropriate.

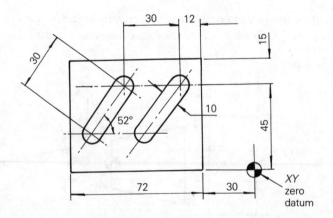

Figure 4.14

12. The component shown in Figure 4.15 is to have two holes drilled in the positions indicated. The programmer has opted to program slide movements in absolute mode from the XY zero datum. In order to program in this way it will be necessary to calculate the linear co-ordinates for one of the holes.

    Sketch the component, carry out the required calculations and dimension your drawing accordingly.

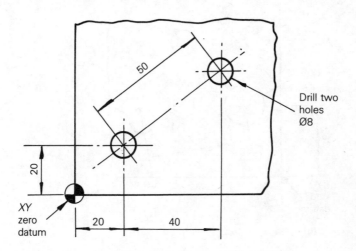

Figure 4.15

13. Calculate and list in programmable form the absolute co-ordinate dimensions in the XY axes necessary to drill the four holes shown in Figure 4.16 in the sequence ABCD, starting and returning to the program datum. Assume that a drill cycle controlling the depth to be drilled is already operative, and may be cancelled by programming G80.

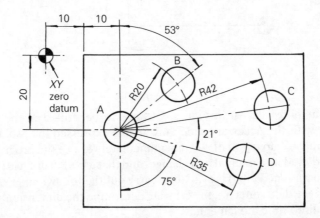

Figure 4.16

14. Figure 4.17(a) shows the position of three holes dimensioned in such a way that is not particularly helpful to the person preparing a part program, since the facility to program polar co-ordinates is not available. The preferred method of dimensioning is indicated in Figure 4.17(b). From the information provided, calculate the missing dimensions.

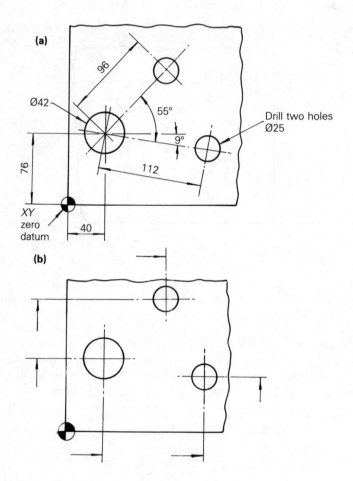

Figure 4.17

15. The four holes shown in Figure 4.18 are to be drilled in the sequence ABCD with the necessary slide movements expressed in absolute terms. Assuming a Z up travel of 200 mm immediately above the program datum to accommodate a manual tool change, and that a G81 drill cycle (cancelled by a programmed G80) is available, carry out the following:
    From the data stated on the drawing determine the dimensional value of the required slide movements.

List the data, in word address format, that would be required to complete the machining, assuming that all speeds, feeds etc. are already operative.

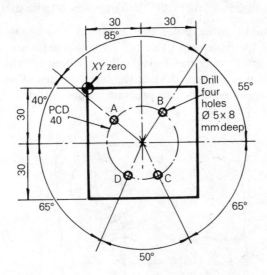

Figure 4.18

16. Eight holes are to be drilled on a pitch circle diameter as shown in Figure 4.19. The holes are to be drilled in the sequence A to H immediately after the central hole has been drilled. Taking the position of the central hole as the zero datum in both the X and Y axes carry out the following:

Calculate the dimensional value of the required slide movements, to facilitate programming in incremental mode.

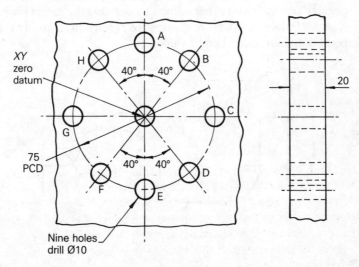

Figure 4.19

List the data as it would be presented in a word address program, assuming a Z datum clearance of 2 mm and an excess travel of 5 mm on breakthrough. Assume that a spindle speed and feed rate have already been programmed and that a G81 drilling cycle is to be used.

17. The position of three holes are given on a drawing as shown in Figure 4.20. The holes are to be drilled in the sequence ABC and the previous program data has brought the machine spindle into vertical alignment with hole A. Calculate the linear values of the incremental moves to be included in the part program to control slide movement in the X and Y axes.

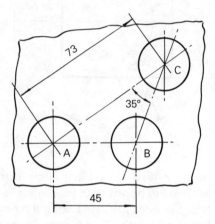

Figure 4.20

18. Complete the program data given below for achieving relative cutter movement from P1 to P2 on the profile illustrated in Figure 4.21. The circular arcs are to be programmed by defining the target positions using X and Y values, and the arc centres are defined in relation to the starting point of the arc using I and J values.

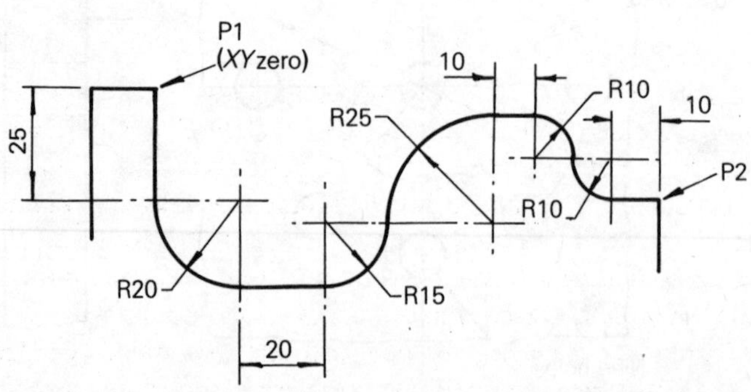

Figure 4.21

N60 G01 Y-25
N70 G03
N80 G01 X20
N90
N100 G02
N110 G01 X10
N120
N130 G03
N140 G01

19. The turned component shown in Figure 4.22 is to be produced on a
     turning centre where arc centres are defined in relation to the program
     datum using the address letters I and K. Complete the program block
     below in incremental terms.

     N 025 G02 X―― Z―― I―― K――

     Repeat the above exercise with the data expressed in absolute terms.

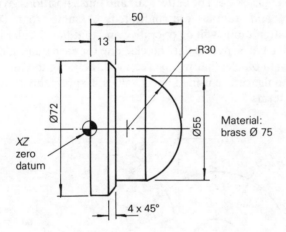

Figure 4.22

20. The concave arc of the turned component shown in Figure 4.23 is to be
     produced on a lathe where the control system will simply require a data
     input stating the radius of the arc, the direction of rotation, and the target
     position defined by X and Z values. Assume that the 8 mm diameter hole
     has already been drilled, and that the curve is to be produced by making
     a cutting pass starting from the centre of the component and working
     outward. Complete the data necessary to machine the feature, with the
     tool starting and finishing in the positions indicated. Assume that a
     suitable cutting speed and feed rate, and also cutter radius compensation,
     are already active.

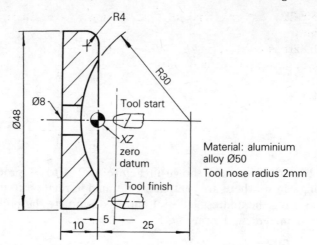

Figure 4.23

21. A cutout of 30 mm radius is to be machined in a 40 mm diameter disc as shown in Figure 4.24. The cutter start and finish positions giving a suitable approach and runout are indicated. Assume that cutter radius compensation mode will be operative and that the circular interpolation will involve two separate data blocks, one for each quadrant. Determine the two data blocks that will be required, defining the arc start point in relation to the centre using I and J values. Express the positional data in absolute terms.

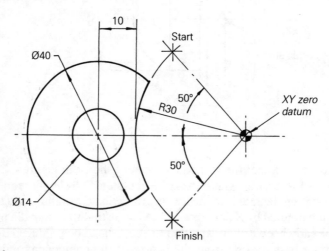

Figure 4.24

22. Figure 4.25 shows a radial slot that is to be machined using a relative cutter movement from the start point to the finish point as indicated.

Calculate the target position in relation to the indicated program datum.

If the start position is to be defined in relation to the arc centre using I and J definition, state their numerical values.

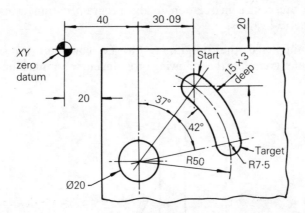

Figure 4.25

23. The two radial slots shown in Figure 4.26 are to be produced on a vertical machining centre, with the starting points as indicated and the relative cutter movement being in a clockwise direction. The control system requires arc centres to be defined in relation to the arc starting point.

Determine the additional dimensional data, in absolute terms, that will be necessary for programming purposes in order to machine the slots.

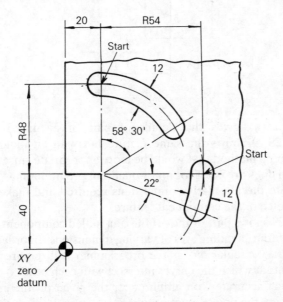

Figure 4.26

24. The turned component in Figure 4.27 is to be produced on a machine fitted with a control system that requires the circular interpolation data entries to be programmed as follows:

   (a) The target position using X and Z numerical values.
   (b) The arc centre in relation to the program datum using I and K numerical values.

   Assuming that the program is to be compiled using absolute dimensions, complete the following program entry for machining the arc:

   N125 G02   X ....   Z ....   I ....   K ....

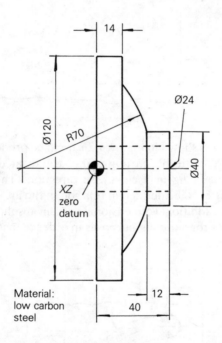

Figure 4.27

25. Figure 4.28(a) gives the details of part of a turned component. Figure 4.28(b) shows the same feature but with an indication of the dimensioning method that would be more appropriate since the machine to be used does not cater for multi-quadrant programming.
   Calculate the alternative dimensions required and make a redimensioned sketch of the component feature.

26. Figure 4.29 shows part of the profile of a milled component. The profile consists of four blending arcs of varying dimensions. In order to program the necessary circular moves the programmer will require to know the exact points at which the curves intersect with each other.
   Construct accurately on graph paper the given profile and locate on your drawing the points of intersection.

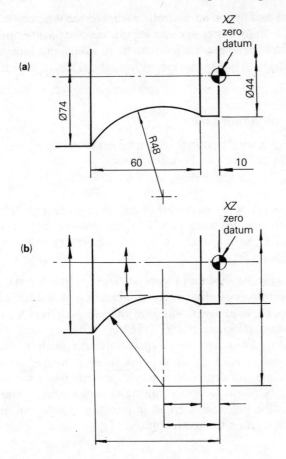

Figure 4.28

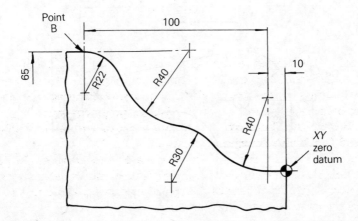

Figure 4.29

Calculate and define numerically each intersection point.

Given the following programming information, list the program data necessary to achieve a cutter path that would machine the profile, commencing with linear movement from the XY zero datum and ending at point B.

Programming information:

G01   Linear interpolation, programmed feed rate.
G02   Circular interpolation, clockwise.
G03   Circular interpolation, counter-clockwise.

Define all target positions incrementally and the arc centres in relation to the arc starting points using I and J values. Assume spindle control data, feed rates etc. have already been programmed and that cutter radius compensation is active.

27. The milled profile shown in Figure 4.30 is to be produced on a machine with a control system that requires numerical definition of the target positions of all slide movements using the address letters X and Y, and arc centres to be defined in relation to the start of the arc using address letters I and J. Also, the system is not capable of multi-quadrant programming, so movement in each quadrant must be programmed separately even when the same radius passes from one quadrant into a second.

Accurately construct the profile and indicate in absolute terms in relation to the program zero all intersection points and also arc start positions in relation to the arc centres.

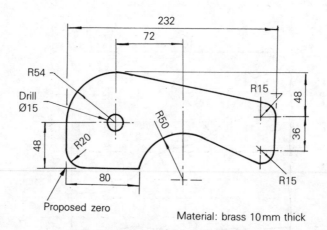

Material: brass 10 mm thick

Figure 4.30

28. The internal profile of the component shown in Figure 4.31 is to be produced on a vertical machining centre. Calculate and indicate on an appropriate sketch the additional dimensions that will be required to define the profile intersection points.

State which common programming facility would be suited to facilitate machining the profile.

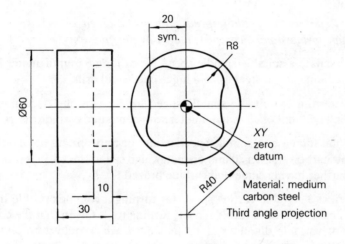

Figure 4.31

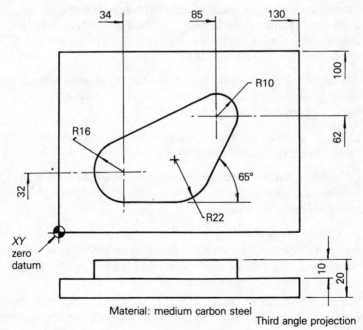

Figure 4.32

29. Figure 4.32 shows details of a milled component.

    Draw the raised profile accurately to size and indicate on your drawing the arc centres and the intersecting points of the profile.

    Calculate all the profile intersecting points required to complete a part program and dimension your drawing accordingly. Assume that arcs can only be programmed for one quadrant in any one block, with the arc centres being specified in relation to the program zero using I and J values.

    Refer to the cutting speeds and feeds given in the Appendices for appropriate data to complete the following questions.

30. Calculate a suitable spindle speed for drilling 6 mm diameter holes in a medium carbon steel using a high speed steel drill.

31. Determine a suitable spindle speed for face cutting duralumin using a shell end mill of 40 mm diameter with cemented carbide insert teeth.

32. What increase in spindle speed would be appropriate if, when drilling a low carbon steel, a 20 mm diameter high speed steel drill is replaced with another having cemented carbide brazed tips?

33. Select a suitable cutting speed for turning a complex profile from brass using a cemented carbide insert turning tool. Given that the component is of variable diameter along its length, why would it be preferable to program a constant surface cutting speed rather than a set spindle speed?

34. Calculate the spindle speed to be used when milling grey cast iron using a 20 mm diameter cemented carbide insert end mill. If the speed calculated eventually proved to be too high, what action should be taken by the machine operator to rectify the situation?

35. Calculate suitable spindle speeds for roughing and finishing cuts when turning duralumin, using cemented carbide tooling on a component having a nominal diameter of 38 mm.

36 Select a suitable feed rate in mm/rev for turning medium carbon steel, using cemented carbide insert tooling.

37. Calculate a suitable feed rate in mm/min for a light turning operation on a stainless steel component having a diameter of 75 mm, and when using cemented carbide tooling.

38. Given that an appropriate feed rate per tooth for face milling a low carbon steel is 0.3 mm per tooth when using cemented carbide tooling, what would be a suitable program entry in mm/min when using a 75 mm diameter cutter having six teeth.

39. The profile shown in Figure 4.33 is of part of a component that is to be machined from brass. The feed rate is to be programmed in mm/rev and

the spindle speed controlled by programming a constant surface cutting speed in m/min.

Select appropriate values for cutting speed and feed to be included in the part program, when using cemented carbide insert tooling.

Using the above combination of data, would the resulting surface finish be identical for both the parallel surfaces and the taper? If not, and assuming that a variation is not acceptable, how could the program be modified?

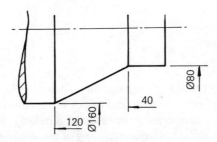

Figure 4.33

40. A face milling operation on aluminium alloy is to be carried out using a nine-cartridge cutter of 100 mm diameter and having cemented carbide inserts. Determine a suitable spindle speed and feed rate in mm/rev for inclusion in the part program.

(For answers, see p.167.)

5

ASSIGNMENTS

Before it is possible to prepare part programs efficiently the programmer must have a full understanding of the capabilities of the machine tools to be used, and the programming and operating procedures. Similarly, if the programming is to be computer assisted a full understanding of the equipment is essential.

The assignments which follow are intended to provide a framework within which the student can, working in conjunction with appropriate demonstrations and explanations provided by the tutor, obtain the necessary information as required.

During these assignments it should be possible for the tutor to emphasise particular aspects of the specific programming tasks that the student will be required to undertake. They will also provide an opportunity to ensure that the student is fully aware of safety precautions that must be observed.

Assignment 1: Tooling and related features

Objective   To examine all aspects of the tooling arrangements for a particular machine, and to determine which aspects have a direct effect on part programming procedure.

Procedure   Using the questions and instructions listed below as a basis, consider each tooling-related feature and make brief but concise notes to which reference can be made, if required, at a later stage. Supplement your notes by including sketches where appropriate.

While some of the information relating to tooling can be obtained by examination of the machine itself and by reference to operating manuals, the most effective and efficient way is certainly via discussion and demonstration by a competent operator of the machine. *On no account must there be experimentation involving machine movement without adequate instruction and supervision.*

Present your findings under a general heading which should include the machine type and the control system. An example of such a heading is given below:

ASSIGNMENT: TOOLING AND RELATED FEATURES
MACHINE: BEAVER TURNING CENTRE TC10
CONTROL SYSTEM: FANUC 10 TF

Questions and instructions

1   Is the tooling available for use with the machine a permanent set-up or is it otherwise restricted in range?

2   If the answer to the above question is positive, list the tools stating their type, size, the material from which each is made and their numerical identities which are to be used for programming purposes.

3   Is the tool-changing process automatic or does it involve manual intervention?

4   If the tool-changing process is automatic describe the action.

5   If the tool-changing process is effected manually, describe the practical involvement of the machine operator. In particular, state the safety aspects that are to be observed during the operation and the way in which the next tool to be used is indicated.

6   Do the machine slides have to be in a particular position before a tool change is effected? If so, note the position.

7   Determine precisely how a tool change is to be programmed. In particular, ascertain whether a safety sub-routine is to be used.

8   Is the tooling for the machine qualified or pre-set?

9   Describe the tool-setting procedures for the machine. In particular, ascertain the means of determining and entering into the machine the offset values that will be invoked via the part program to compensate for variations in tool length and/or diameter or radius.

10   Describe the method used within the program to pair offset values with tool calls. Note the number of offsets available in relation to the number of tools that are to be used. Since there are likely to be more possible offsets than there are tools, ascertain how alternative pairings can be used within the part program, and the machining objectives that can be achieved by such pairings.

11   If offset/tool pairings are to be used to achieve specific machining objectives, describe the means used to convey the information from the part programmer to the machine setter/operator.

12 Find out how cutter radius compensation is included in the part program, and how to determine whether the compensation is to the right or left of a profile and how it is cancelled.

Assignment 2: Work-holding and location

Objective   To examine all aspects of work-holding on a particular machine, and to determine which aspects have a direct effect on part programming procedure.

Procedure   Using the questions and instructions listed below as a basis, consider each work-holding feature and make brief but concise notes to which reference can be made, if required, at a later stage. Supplement your notes by including sketches where appropriate.

While some information relating to work-holding can be obtained by examination of the machine itself and possibly by reference to operating manuals, the most effective and efficient way is certainly via discussion and demonstration by a competent operator of the machine.

Present your findings under a general heading which should include the machine type and the control system. An example of such a heading is to be found at the beginning of Assignment 1.

Questions and instructions

1   What work-holding devices are available for use on the machine?

2   Are there any special operating instructions to be observed when using the available work-holding devices? For example, the use of a hand controlled hydraulically operated vice may be subject to a specific operating pressure.

3   Are there any special fail-safe arrangements associated with the work-holding arrangements that will be used? For example, if the device happens to be air operated what will happen if there is a loss of air pressure?

4   Does the machine have a fixed zero datum? If so, note the position.

5   If the machine zero datum is a fixed position can it be repositioned on a temporary basis via a zero shift facility?

6   If a zero shift facility is available describe how the amount of shift is determined and how it is entered into the control system.

7   Is it possible to establish more than one zero shift?

8   How is a zero shift activated via the part program?

9   If the machine has a floating zero describe how zero is established.

10   It is imperative that there is some correlation between the location of a workpiece and established zero datum positions. What information will be

required to ensure the workpiece is correctly positioned before a machining program is undertaken?

11 If the machine being studied is equipped with ancillary or supplementary work-holding or supporting devices, determine if there are any specific instructions to be observed regarding their use. In particular, if the devices are programmable, determine how their use relates to part programming procedure.

12 Determine if there are any specific safety precautions to be observed when loading or unloading work pieces.

Assignment 3: Data processing

Objective To provide an appreciation of the data entry, editing, transmission and storage facilities associated with a particular machine.

Procedure Using the following questions and practical tasks as a basis, carry out a detailed examination of the way in which data is processed and make notes of specific points that will be of value at a later stage.

Demonstration of the equipment by a competent person, supported by discussion, will be essential. A previously prepared sample part program will also be required.

Present your findings under a general heading which should include the machine type and the control system. An example of such a heading is given at the beginning of Assignment 1.

Questions and instructions

1 Describe the way in which the machine is prepared for data entry—the power-up procedure.

2 Is the programming concept for the machine conversational MDI or word address, or can both be accommodated?

3 If the controller can be used for both conversational MDI and word address describe the preparation procedures involved.

4 What is the capacity, in terms of permissible blocks, of the control system?

5 Is there a battery back-up to protect against the loss of program data in the event of a power failure?

6 How many ways can data be entered into the control system?

7 How many ways can data be extracted from the control system?

8 Describe the program proving facilities available on the machine.

9 List the procedures, with particular reference to safety, that must be adopted when carrying out program proving on the machine.

10 Enter a sample part program into the machine controller via the keyboard.

11 Make specified amendments to the previously entered part program. This task should incorporate editing features such as block search, block deletion, block insertion etc.

12 If the facility is available, carry out a test run of the program bearing in mind any safety precautions that are to be observed.

13 Carry out a dry run of the program bearing in mind any safety precautions that are to be observed. Part of this test should be completed on a 'single block' basis and part on an 'automatic' basis.

14 Connect a tape punch to the machine and extract the part program from the memory; at the same time, if possible, make a printout of the data. Alternatively, record the program on magnetic tape.

15 Re-enter the part program into the machine via perforated tape or magnetic tape. If the machine has both facilities then both systems should be used.

16 If the machine is part of a Direct Numerical Control (DNC) set-up determine the procedures for transferring data to and from the off-line programming facility.

Assignment 4: Computer aided part programming facilities

Objective To provide an appreciation of the computer installation and the associated peripheral equipment that is to be used for computer aided part programming.

Procedure Using the following questions and instructions as a basis, carry out an examination of the equipment to be used. To assist this exercise demonstration of the equipment by a competent person will be essential.

Present your findings under a general heading such as the example given below:

ASSIGNMENT: COMPUTER AIDED PART PROGRAMMING
                FACILITIES
COMPUTERS: OLIVETTI M24 MICROS
SOFTWARE: CADMASS

Questions and instructions

1 List the stages involved in programming a machine tool control unit using the CAPP facility being studied.

2 How many work stations are available?

3 Are the work stations stand-alone or networked?

4 List the methods available for the input of data to the computer.

5 List the methods available for the storage of data.

6 List the peripheral equipment available for use in the programming facility.

7 Are the peripheral devices part of a network?

8 If the peripheral devices are not part of a network, how are they brought into use?

9 How many post processors are there for use within the facility, and what machine tools do they serve?

10 Is there a direct cable link from the CAPP facility to all, or any, of the machines for which there are post processors?

11 What arrangements are there, other than a direct cable link, for the transfer of data to the machine tools?

12 Using the information gathered in response to the above questions construct a block diagram, similar to that on page 96, to represent the complete system that will be used, showing each item of hardware and a clear indication of how data is transmitted.

13 What is the procedure to be adopted to prepare the work station for part programming?

14 Describe in detail the procedure adopted to facilitate data storage by any method, or methods, other than a perforated tape or printout.

15 Describe in detail the procedure adopted to facilitate the production of a perforated tape.

16 Describe in detail the procedure for producing a printout of data.

17 Describe in detail the procedure for producing a plot of the geometric detail of the part and the related cutter paths.

18 Describe in detail the procedure for transferring data between the programming facility and the machine tools via a direct cable link.

19 If there is insufficient time to complete a part program, what procedure is adopted to store data so that it will be possible to complete the work at a later time?

20 Are there any special instructions to be followed regarding closing down the system after use?

6

PART PROGRAMMING PROJECTS

The following pages contain a series of detail drawings of engineering components. The design of these components is such that they will present the student with problems, both in relation to part programming and general machining techniques of a fairly high standard.

It is intended that each component, or in some cases each series of related components, will be used as the basis of a comprehensive CNC machining project. The project would also give full consideration to the topics discussed elsewhere in this text, namely process planning, work holding, tooling, part programming and so on. Ideally, the final stage in the project should be the machining of the component.

Two problem areas are likely to present themselves. It is possible that the student will be hampered by a lack of practical machining experience; it is also possible that he or she may lack the necessary mathematical ability.

There is no easy solution to the first problem—the student not having the necessary knowledge of machining techniques. It is an essential element of successful CNC part programming, but it can only be acquired by experience gained on the shop floor.

Shortcomings in mathematical ability can, up to a point, be overcome with the aid of a computer and appropriate software. However, the programmer will still find it is essential to have a sound background in geometric construction.

The stage at which a part programmer should resort to the help of a computer is open to question—rather like whether a calculator should be used to do simple calculations that could readily be carried out using pen and paper. It could be strongly argued that if a facility is available it should be used and, indeed, it is likely that the bulk of CNC part programming in the future will be carried out with the aid of a computer.

We are, however, passing through a transitional stage and students are likely to find themselves operating in a CNC programming situation where recourse to computing assistance is not possible. It is therefore prudent to develop an ability in manual programming alongside the ability to perform computer aided programming.

Thus in selecting components to be programmed as part of an overall CNC production project the student is strongly advised to undertake the programming of at least one component on a manual basis. It is, incidentally, a requirement of the City and Guilds 230 CNC Advanced Part Programming Course that one practical assignment should involve manual programming.

It is possible that the drawings which follow present mathematical problems that are not within the student's ability, and that less complex components may be more appropriate. There are a number of fully dimensioned components throughout the text that may be used as an alternative. These components are listed on page 166.

The student is again reminded of the need to support his or her part programming efforts with documentation relating to machine setting and tooling. If such work is to be submitted for assessment clear and concise presentation is essential.

Finally, the need to adopt a logical approach to a part programming task cannot be stressed too strongly. Reference to Chapter 2, page 42, where the various related stages of the part programming process are listed, may be appropriate.

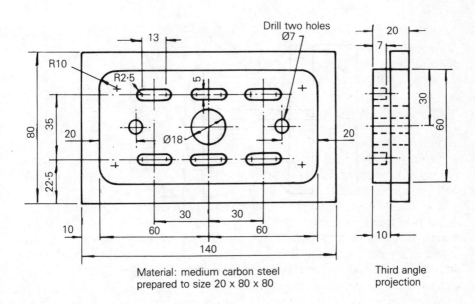

Material: medium carbon steel
prepared to size 20 x 80 x 80

Third angle
projection

Project 1

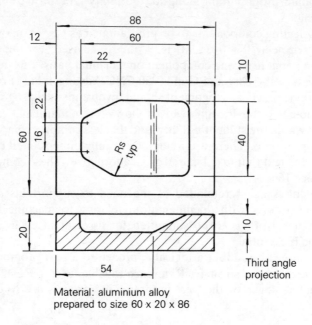

Material: aluminium alloy
prepared to size 60 x 20 x 86

Project 2

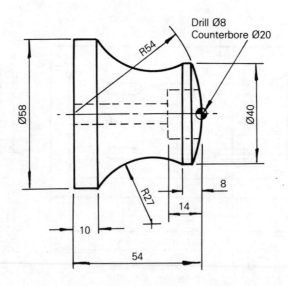

Material: mild steel, 60 mm diameter.

Project 3

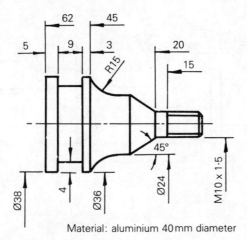

Material: aluminium 40 mm diameter

Project 4

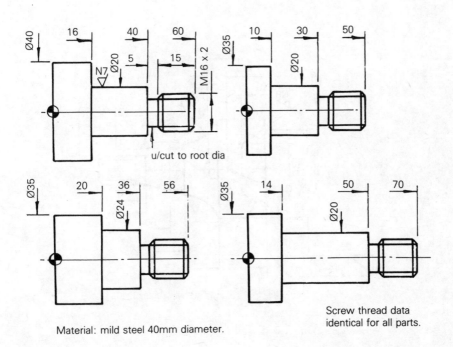

Material: mild steel 40mm diameter.

Screw thread data identical for all parts.

Project 5 *Note: This project is intended for parametric programming*

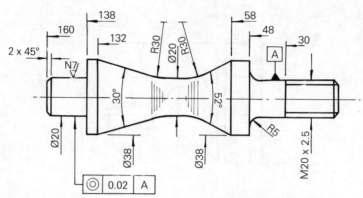

Material: medium carbon steel
40 mm diameter

Project 6

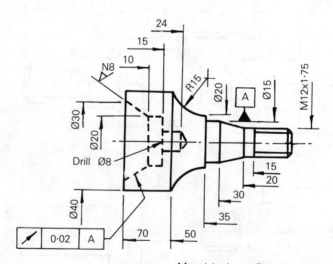

Materials: brass Ø40

Project 7

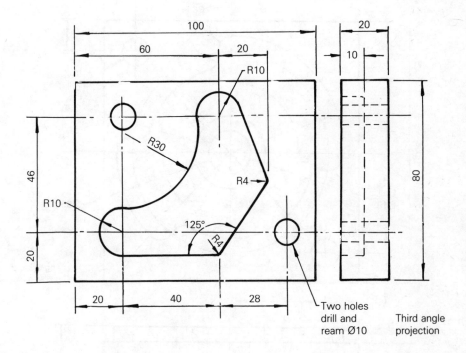

Material: medium carbon steel prepared 20 x 80 x 100

Project 8

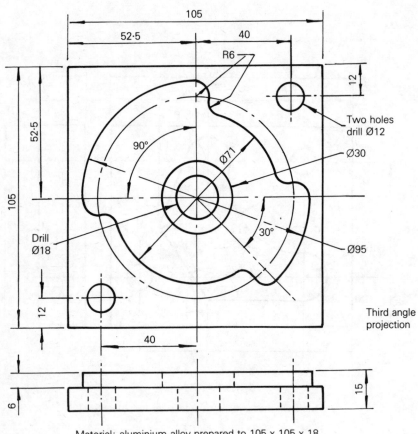

Third angle
projection

Material: aluminium alloy prepared to 105 x 105 x 18

Project 9

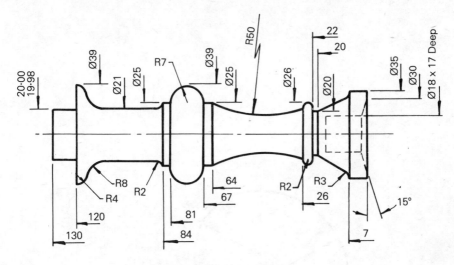

Material: brass 40 mm diameter.

Project 10   *Note: This component assembles with Project 11*

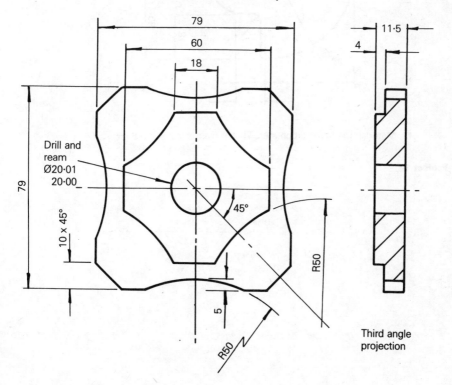

Material: brass prepared to size 80 x 12

Project 11   *Note: This component assembles with Project 10*

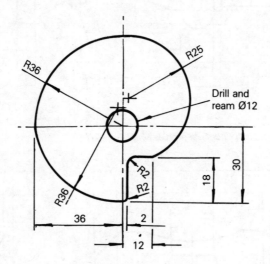

Material: medium carbon steel 75 mm diameter x 8 mm thick.

Project 12

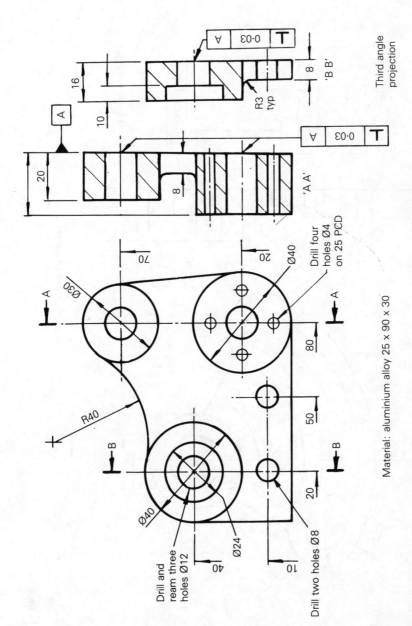

Third angle
projection

'B B'

'A A'

Material: aluminium alloy 25 x 90 x 30

Drill four
holes Ø4
on 25 PCD

Drill and
ream three
holes Ø12

Drill two holes Ø8

Project 13

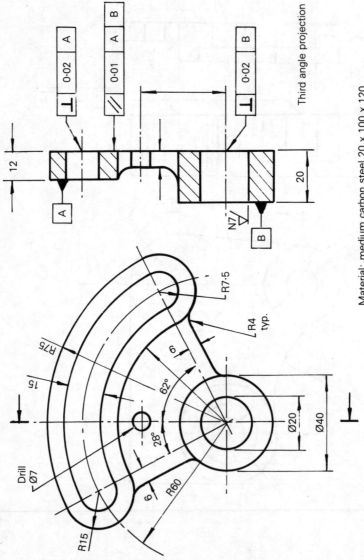

Third angle projection

Material: medium carbon steel 20 x 100 x 120

Project 14

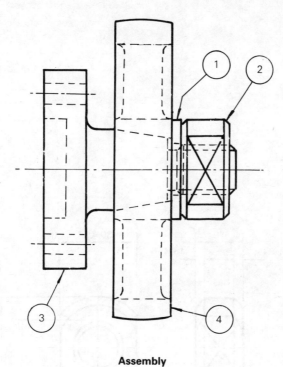

Assembly

Project 15

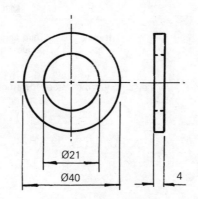

Ø21

Ø40

4

Material: low carbon steel 40 mm diameter

Item 1

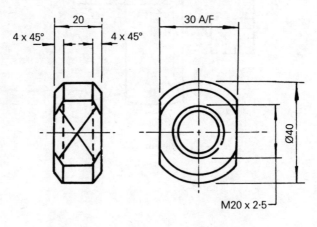

20

4 x 45°   4 x 45°

30 A/F

Ø40

M20 x 2·5

Item 2   Third angle
projection

Material: low carbon steel 40 mm diameter

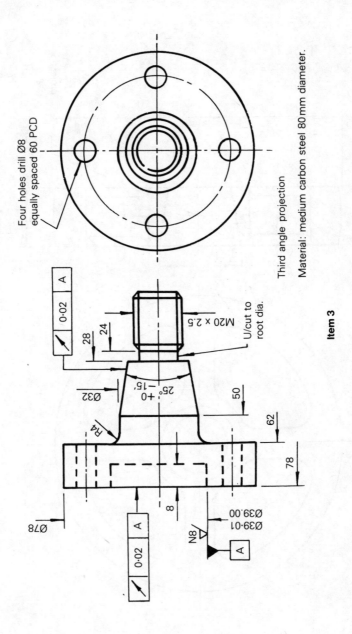

Four holes drill Ø8
equally spaced 60 PCD

Third angle projection

Material: medium carbon steel 80 mm diameter.

M20 × 2.5

U/cut to
root dia.

28

24

$25° {}^{+0}_{-15'}$

Ø32

50

62

78

R4

Ø78

8

Ø39·01
Ø39.00

N8

0·02 | A

0·02 | A

A

Item 3

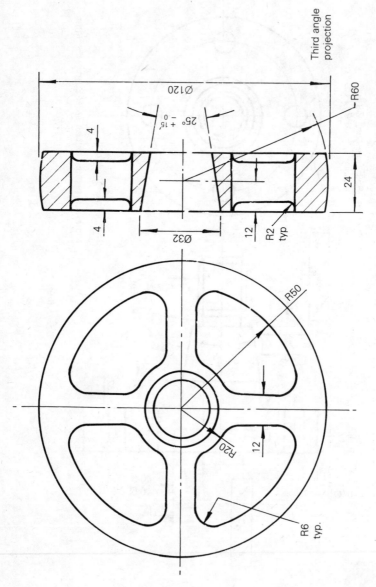

Third angle projection

Ø120

25° $+ \, 15' \atop - \, 0'$

4

4

Ø32

12

R2 typ

24

R60

R50

R20

12

R6 typ.

Material: medium carbon steel 125 mm diameter.
Machine all over.

Item 4

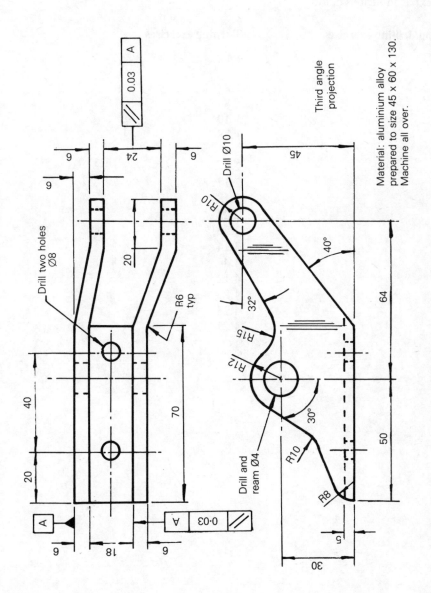

Third angle projection

Material: aluminium alloy
prepared to size 45 x 60 x 130.
Machine all over.

Drill Ø10

Drill two holes
Ø8

R6
typ

Drill and
ream Ø4

R10

R15

R12

R10

R8

32°

40°

30°

Project 16

Alternative introductory programming exercises

Details of components which are generally less complex than those which follow, and may in some cases be more appropriate, are included elsewhere in the text as indicated below.

Milling/drilling exercises	Turning exercises
Figure	*Figure*
1.3	1.2
1.9	1.8
2.2	1.10
2.9	1.38
2.12	2.4
2.28	2.6
3.11	2.17
4.5	2.18
4.6	2.22
4.7	2.26
4.8	3.14
4.30	4.4
4.31	4.12
4.32	4.22
	4.23
	4.27

ANSWERS TO CHAPTER 4

1   X axis dimensions as given plus Ø62 and Ø86
    Z axis dimensions: 10, 18, 30, 56, 60 mm

2   X axis dimensions: 14, 40, 68, 79(2), 87, 99 mm
    Y axis dimensions: 10, 20, 30, 50, 60 mm

3   (i) Alternative sequence: AFEDCB
    (ii) 34 min

4   FDBACE

5   (i) ADCECFGFHI or IHFGFCECDA
    (ii) 35.67 sec

6   Various solutions possible.

7   Various solutions possible.

8   X0 Y0
    X11 Y−33.645
    X62.645 Y62.645
    X−73.645 Y−29

9   X axis increment: 6 mm
    Z axis increment: 22.228 mm

10 Z axis dimensions: 26.807, 63.264 mm

11 X axis dimensions: 90.47, 72, 60.47, 42 mm
    Y axis dimension: 21.36 mm

12 X axis dimension: 60 mm
    Y axis dimension: 50 mm

13 X20 Y−20
    X35.973 Y−7.964
    X61.77 Y−15.61
    X53.807 Y−29.059
    G80 X0 Y0

14 X axis dimensions: 106.687, 150.621 mm
    Y axis dimensions: 58.48, 145.056 mm

15 G00 Z2
G81 Z−10
X14.679 Y−17.144
X41.472 Y−13.617
X38.452 Y−48.126
X21.548 Y−48.126
G80 X0 Y0 Z200

16 G81 Z−27
X0 Y0
Y37.5
X24.105 Y−8.773
X13.395 Y−28.727
X−13.395 Y−28.727
X−24.105 Y−8.773
X−24.105 Y8.773
X−13.395 Y28.727
X13.395 Y28.727
G80 X0 Y0

17 From A to B: X45
From B to C: X14.152 Z46.109

18 G01 Y−25
G03 X20 Y−20 I20
G01 X20
G03 X15 Y15 J15
G02 X25 Y25 I25
G01 X10
G03 X10 Y−10 J10
G03 X10 Y−10 I10
G01 X10

19 (i) N025 G02 X27.5 Z−18.01 I0 K20
(ii) N025 G02 X55 Z31.989 I0 K20
(Assumes diameter programming)

20 G01 Z−5
G03 X40.792 Z3 R30 CCW

21 G03 X−30 Y0 I19.284 J22.981
G03 X−19.284 Y−22.981 I30

22 X89.081 Y−50.392 I 30.09 J39.932

23 Upper slot:
G02 X60.927 Y65.080 J48
Lower slot:
G02 X70.068 Y19.771 I54

24 N125 G02 X91.264 Z14 I20 K−39.082
(Assumes diameter programming)

25 X axis dimensions: Ø74, Ø34.232, Ø44, and 43.116 mm
Z axis dimensions: 70, 31.096, 21.096, 10 mm
R48

26 G01 X−10
G02 X−31.169 Y14.93 J40
G03 X−18.015 Y10.715 I23.377 J18.802
G02 X−30.252 Y25.161 I7.145 J39.356
G03 X−20.569 Y14.194 I20.569 K7.805

27 (ii) Profile intersection points working clockwise from zero:

X0	Y20
X0	Y48
X54	Y102
X64.978	Y100.872
X220.049	Y68.680
X232	Y54
X232	Y18
X217	Y3
X212.15	Y3.806
X142.168	Y27.718
X126	Y30.044
X80	Y0
X20	Y0

Hole centre:

X54	Y48

Arc start to arc centre values:

R54 I54 ⎫
R54 J54 ⎭ (two moves)
R15 (upper) I3.049 J14.686
R15 (lower) I15 ⎫
R15 (lower) J15 ⎭ (two moves)
R50 I16.167 J47.314 ⎫
R50 J50 ⎭ (two moves)
R20 J20

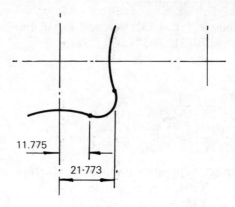

11.775

21·773

Figure A 1

28 The numerical data given above is repeated twice for each quadrant.

29 Profile intersection points, starting at bottom of R16 and working clockwise:

X34	Y16
X18	Y32
X27.327	Y46.54
X80.829	Y71.089
X85	Y72
X95	Y62
X94.063	Y57.774
X80.507	Y28.702
	X60.568

Arc start to arc centre values:
R16 I34 J32
R10 I85 J62
R22 I60.568 J38

Note: The answers given below are typical. Precise answers will depend on the data selected by the student from the data sheets in Appendices 2, 3 and 4.

30 1060 rev/min

31 1500 rev/min

32 From 560 rev/min to 2000 rev/min

33 230 m/min. A set spindle speed would not be efficient for all diameters.

34 2300 rev/min. If programmed speed proved to be too high the machine operator should adjust via the spindle speed override facility and notify the programmer of the need to do so.

35 Roughing: 2100 rev/min
Finishing: 3500 rev/min. Note that the spindle speed for finishing is likely
to be restricted to the maximum speed available on the machine.

36 0.25 mm/rev

37 200 mm/min

38 1500 mm/min

39 (i) 230 m/min, 0.5 mm/rev
(ii) Variations in surface finish are possible. May be rectified by
programming constant surface cutting speed and reduced feed rate for
machining taper.

40 Spindle speed: 2228 rev/min
Feed: 3 mm/rev

APPENDICES

APPENDIX 1

Standard tape codes

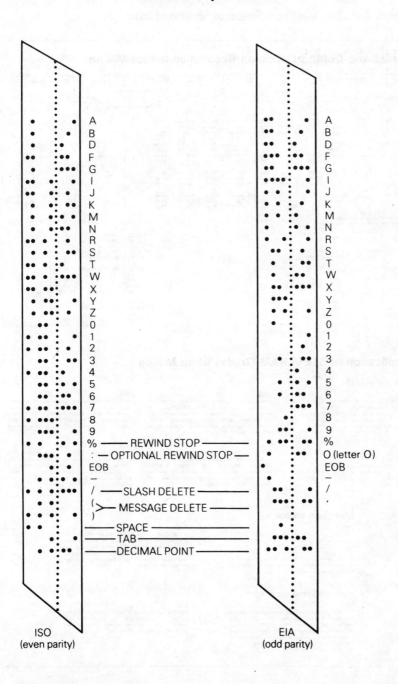

ISO
(even parity)

EIA
(odd parity)

APPENDIX 2

Cutting data for milling

(Reproduced by kind permission of Stellram Ltd)

Grades and Cutting Condition Recommended for Milling

STELLRAM grades	Hardness HB	Strength Rm N/mm²	S2F 0,2-0,6	S2F 0,05-0,3	SF30 0,3-0,6	SF30 0,1-0,3	S6X7 0,3-0,8	H1X 0,2-0,6	GH1 0,2-0,5	GH1 0,05-0,3	GH2 0,2-1,0	X44 0,3-1,2	X22 0,3-1,2
Carbon steel C = <0,4%	–	≤ 600	150-120 ①	300-180 ②	200-150 ①	250-200 ②	130-70					200-140	
C = 0,4-0,7%		600-800	140-110	280-170	120-100	170-120	110-60					140-100	
C = 0,7-1,0%		800-1000	120-90	250-150	110-80	140-110	80-50					100-50	
Stainless steel Ferrit. Cr 12-18%	150-250		140-100	250-170	120-100	170-120	110-50					140-100	
18/8			130-90	230-150	110-80	140-110	80-50					120-70	
Martensit. Cr 12-15%	>250		120-80	220-140	110-80	140-110	75-50					90-30	
			110-60				60-35						
Cast steel	< 150	< 500	140-90	280-170	120-100	160-120	90-60					120-60	
	150-250	600-800	120-80	250-150	110-80	140-110	80-50					100-50	
	250-300	> 900	100-70	220-120	110-80	140-110	60-40					80-40	
Alloyed steel annealed		500-800	140-90	260-170	110-90	150-110	90-40					100-40	100-40
hardened		700-850	120-80	230-150	90-70	120-90	80-40					90-40	90-40
		850-1100	100-70	200-120	70-50	100-70	60-30					60-40	60-40
High alloy steel, heat resistant steel, stainless steel, austenitic steel		600-1200	150-80				60-40	90-60		220-150	120-10	60-40	100-10
Gray cast iron	≤ 250							140-80	140-80	250-180	100-50		
	250-300							120-60	120-60	220-150	70-40		
Spheroidal cast iron Ferrit.	140-180							120-70	120-70	220-160	80-50		
Perlit.	230-280							100-60	100-60	200-140	70-40		
Malleable cast iron	160-240							140-80	140-80	250-180	90-40		
Alluminium and alloys soft	50-140							800-600	800-600		700-400		
hard	90-140							250-150	250-150		150-80		
Si-aluminium alloys cast								1000-700	1000-700		800-500		
Copper and brass soft								500-150	500-150		400-100		
drawn, rolled								600-250	600-250		450-150		
Synthetic materials								250-180	250-180		140-80		

Feed per tooth (mm/tooth) given in column sub-headings; Cutting speed (m/min) given in cells.

① Standard cutting speeds ② high cutting speeds

Application of STELLRAM Grades when Milling

Standard grades

SOEX
Available as finishing inserts for inter-changeable cartridges on Stellram milling cutters 7800v and 8000v. This grade is suitable for finishing and super-finishing components on carbon steel, cast steel and alloyed steel with cutting speeds of 140/250 m/min.

SF30
General purpose milling grade for roughing and semi-finishing with cutting speeds of 50-200 m/min. Recommended for use on carbon steel, cast steel, alloyed steel and stainless steel.

GS07
Available as finishing inserts for inter-changeable cartridges on Stellram milling cutters 7800v and 8000v. This grade is suitable for finishing and super-finishing components on gray cast iron, malleable cast iron, spheroidal cast iron and non ferrous light metals and alloys, at cutting speeds 140/250 m/min.

S2F
General purpose milling grade for roughing, semi-finishing and finishing, at cutting speeds either standard 80-180 m/min or high speed 160-280 m/min. Suitable for machining carbon steel, cast steel, alloyed steel, stainless steel, martensitic steel and manganese steel.

S6X7
Used primarily for roughing operations and other operations under difficult conditions, e.g. components with holes, insufficient rigidity of the machine or the workpiece holding system, vibrations etc. Recommended for carbon steel, alloyed steel, cast steel of low or average strength.

H1X
Is suitable for light roughing, semi-finishing and finishing, on gray cast iron or malleable cast iron which produces short swarf, with cutting speeds of 60-120 m/min. It is also an extremely good standard grade for aluminium and alloys, copper, brass, bronze and synthetic materials with cuttings speeds 250-1000 m/min.

Micrograin grades

GH1
Is suitable for light roughing, semi-finishing and finishing, on gray cast iron, malleable cast iron, which produces short swarf and chilled iron castings, with standard cutting speeds 100-150 m/min or high cutting speeds 180-250 m/min. This grade gives exceptional results on light alloys and synthetic materials and is also suitable for finishing on heat resistant alloys.

GH2
Is most suited to roughing operations and other difficult operations e.g. components with holes, insufficient rigidity, vibration etc. It was developed for use on cast iron, but will give excellent results on austenitic stainless steel, titanium alloys and heat resistant alloys (Waspaloy, Inconel, Stellite, etc.).

High performance grades

X44
Has been specially formulated in respect of the binding material and structure, resulting in an extremely tough carbide. It works well in difficult machining conditions e.g. severe interrupted cutting, shock loading, vibrations, lack of rigidity etc. on high strength structural steel, cast steel with sand inclusions and voids, alloyed steel and stainless steel up to 12% Co + Ni.

X22
Was developed in the same manner as X44, it is suitable for heavy roughing operations on titanium alloys, heat resistant alloys e.g. Waspaloy, Inconel, Nimonic, Stellite etc. as well as austenitic stainless steel.

APPENDIX 2.2

Tooling Grades

ISO GROUPS	Standard		Micrograin	Special Micrograin
P01	**SOex** TiC + TaC 34% Co 7% 82HRc 1600 N/mm²			
P05				
P10		**S2F** TiC + TaC 20,5% Co 10% 79 HRc 2100 N/mm²		
P15				
P20				
P25		**SF30** TiC + TaC 20,5% Co 10% 79,5HRc 2200 N/mm²		**X44** TiC + TaC 19% Co 12% 79 HRc 2400 N/mm²
P30				
P35			**GH2**	
P40	**S6X7** TiC + TaC 18% Co 14% 77 HRc 2250 N/mm²			
P50				
M05		**GSO-7** TiC + TaC 11% Co 6% 83HRc 1750 N/mm²		
M10			**GH1**	
M15				
M20	**S6X7**		**GH2**	**X22**
M30				
M40			**GH1**	
K01		**GSO-7**		
K05			**GH1** TiC + TaC 0% Co 6% 82,5 HRc 2050 N/mm²	
K10	**H1X** TiC + TaC 1% Co 5% 82 HRc 1800 N/mm²			
K15				
K20				
K25			**GH2** TiC + TaC 0% Co 9,5% 80 HRc 2400 N/mm²	**X22** TiC + TaC 0% Co 8% 81 HRc 2500 N/mm²
K30				
K40				
K50				

SO ex for special applications only

APPENDIX 3

Cutting data for turning

(Reproduced by kind permission of Anderson Strathclyde PLC)

MATERIAL	SPEED FT/MIN M/MIN			FEED INS/REV MM/REV			DEPTH INS MM			GRADE	
	ROUGH		FINISH	ROUGH	FINISH		ROUGH		FINISH	ROUGH	FINISH
ALUMINIUM ALLOYS	800	1600	2500	.04	.02	.008	.25	.18	.01	CG	CF
	250	500	750	1.	.5	.2	6.5	4.5	.25		
ALUMINIUM CASTINGS	800	1600	2500	.04	.02	.008	.25	.18	.01	CG	CF
	250	500	750	1.	.5	.2	6.5	4.5	.25		
ALUMINIUM CASTINGS, HT. TREATED	300	600	1600	.04	.02	.008	.25	.18	.01	CG	CF
	90	180	500	1.	.5	.2	6.5	4.5	.25		
BRASS	600	750	1000	.04	.02	.008	.25	.18	.01	CG	CF
	180	230	300	1.	.5	.2	6.5	4.5	.25		
BRONZE, PHOSPHOR	300	600	800	.04	.02	.008	.25	.18	.01	CG	CF
	90	180	250	1.	.5	.2	6.5	4.5	.25		
CAST IRON, ALLOY	150	350	500	.04	.02	.008	.25	.18	.01	CR	CG
	45	105	150	1.	.5	.2	6.5	4.5	.25		
CAST IRON, CHILLED 400B	30	60	100	.04	.02	.008	.25	.18	.01	CG	CG
	9	18	30	1.	.5	.2	6.5	4.5	.25		
CAST IRON, CHILLED 600B	25	50	60	.04	.02	.008	.25	.18	.01	CG	CG
	8	15	18	1.	.5	.2	6.5	4.5	.25		
CAST IRON, GREY	250	550	650	.04	.02	.008	.3	.2	.01	CR	CG
	75	165	190	1.	.5	.2	7.5	5.	.25		
CAST IRON, NODULAR, FERRITIC	150	300	500	.04	.02	.008	.2	.1	.01	CR	CG
	45	90	150	1.	.5	.2	5.	2.5	.25		
CAST IRON, NODULAR, PEARLITIC	150	300	450	.04	.02	.008	.2	.1	.01	CR	CG
	45	90	135	1.	.5	.2	5.	2.5	.25		
COPPER	600	1100	2000	.04	.02	.008	.25	.18	.01	CR	CG
	180	330	600	1.	.5	.2	6.5	4.5	.25		
FIBRE	300	500	700	.04	.02	.008	.25	.18	.01	CG	CF
	90	150	210	1.	.5	.2	6.5	4.5	.25		
HARD RUBBER, ASBESTOS	600	800	1000	.04	.02	.008	.3	.2	.01	CF	CF
	180	250	300	1.	.5	.2	7.5	5.	.25		
LEAD BRONZE, ALLOY	750	1000	1500	04	.02	.008	.25	.18	.01	CW	CG
	230	300	450	1.	.5	.2	6.5	4.5	.25		

MATERIAL	SPEED FT/MIN M/MIN			FEED INS/REV MM/REV			DEPTH INS MM			GRADE	
	ROUGH		FINISH	ROUGH		FINISH	ROUGH		FINISH	ROUGH	FINISH
MALLEABLE IRON, LONG CHIP	150	500	650	.04	.02	.008	.3	.2	.01	M1	M1
	45	150	190	1.	.5	.2	7.5	5.	.25		
MALLEABLE IRON, SHORT CHIP	250	400	600	.04	.02	.008	.3	.2	.01	M1/1	M1/1
	75	120	180	1.	.5	.2	7.5	5.	.25		
PORCELAIN	50	60	80	.04	.02	.008	.1	.01	.003	CF	CF
	15	18	25	1.	.5	.2	2.5	.25	.08		
RIGID PLASTICS, WOOD	600	800	1300	.04	.02	.008	.3	.2	.01	CW	CF
	180	250	390	1.	.5	.2	7.5	5.	.25		
STEEL, ALLOY, ANNEALED	300	500	650	.03	.01	.004	.5	.25	.015	SG	SF
	90	150	190	.75	.25	.1	13.	6.5	.4		
STEEL, ALLOY, HARDENED 250B	250	400	600	.03	.01	.004	.3	.2	.01	SG	SF
	75	120	180	.75	.25	.1	7.5	5.	.25		
STEEL, ALLOY, HARDENED 300B	200	300	500	.03	.01	.004	.25	.18	.01	SG	SF
	60	90	150	.75	.25	.1	6.5	4.5	.25		
STEEL, ALLOY, HARDENED 400B	150	250	350	.03	.01	.004	.25	.18	.01	SG	SF
	45	75	100	.75	.25	.1	6.5	4.5	.25		
STEEL, CARBON NORMALISED 125B	600	800	1100	.03	.01	.004	.5	.25	.015	SG	SF
	180	250	330	.75	.25	.1	13.	6.5	.4		
STEEL, CARBON NORMALISED 150B	400	650	1000	.03	.01	.004	.5	.25	.015	SG	SF
	120	190	300	.75	.25	.1	13.	6.5	.4		
STEEL, CARBON NORMALISED 250B	300	500	650	.03	.01	.004	.3	.2	.01	SG	SF
	90	150	190	.75	.25	.1	7.5	5.	.25		
STEEL, CAST 150B	200	300	500	.05	.01	.006	.5	.25	.015	SG	SF
	60	90	150	1.25	.25	.15	13.	6.5	.4		
STEEL, CAST 250B	150	250	350	.05	.01	.006	.3	.2	.01	SG	SF
	45	75	100	1.25	.25	.15	7.5	5.	.25		
STEEL, MANGANESE	60	100	200	.04	.02	.008	.3	.2	.01	CW	CG
	18	30	60	1.	.5	.2	7.5	5.	.25		
STEEL, STAINLESS, AUSTENTIC	300	400	500	.08	.015	.008	.25	.18	.01	CW	CW
	90	120	150	2.	.4	.2	6.5	4.5	.25		
STEEL, STAINLESS, MARTENSITIC	300	400	600	.08	.015	.008	.25	.18	.01	SG	SF
	90	120	180	2.	.4	.2	6.5	4.5	.25		
STEEL, TOOL, HARDENED	30	60	100	.04	.02	.008	.2	.1	.01	SG	SF
	9	18	30	1.	.5	.2	5.	2.5	.25		
STONE, HARD GRANITE	25	35	50	.04	.02	.008	.2	.1	.01	CR	CR
	8	10	15	1.	.5	.2	5.	2.5	.25		
STONE, SOFT MARBLE	150	200	250	.04	.02	.008	.2	.1	.01	CF	CF
	45	60	75	1.	.5	.2	5.	2.5	.25		

APPENDIX 3.2

Tooling grades

HOYBIDE GRADE	WORKPIECE MATERIAL AND OPERATION	ISO CODE	COLOUR CODE
SG	For all general purpose steel cutting operations, with the exceptions of stainless steels, high-nickel alloys and heat and creep-resistant alloys.	P20	Blue
CG	For all machining operations on cast irons, meehanite, non-ferrous metals and short-chip alloy irons.	K20	Red
CW	For machining stainless steels, high-nickel alloys and heat and creep-resistant alloys. It can also be used as a universal grade for steels, cast irons, non-ferrous metals, plastics, wood, etc.	P30 M30 K20 K30	Yellow
GT	TiN coated, for machining steels, stainless steel, and general purpose operations on other metals at higher speeds with longer tool life.	P20 P30 P35 K20	Gold

The grades shown above are normally stocked in a wide range of sizes of square, triangular and rhombic, clamp and pin type, negative and positive rake conventional inserts.

APPENDIX 4

Cutting data for drilling

(Reproduced by kind permission of Guhring Ltd)

Material of workpiece	Drill type	Material of drill	Point angle	Cutting speed m per min.	Feed scale No. (see Fig.A4.1)	Coolant
Free-cutting mild steel hardness up to 500 N/mm²	N/GT 50	HSS	118°	30 – 50	4	Soluble oil
Non-alloyed carbon steel with ≤ 0.4% carbon ≤ 800 N/mm	N	HSS	118	20 – 30	4	Soluble oil
Non-alloyed carbon steel with ≥ 0.4% carbon, hardness 800–1000 N/mm² and purified alloy steel with a hardness ≤ 700 N/mm²	N/GT 100	HSS	118°	16 – 20	3	Soluble oil
Non-alloyed tool steels with a hardness of 800–1000 N/mm² and refined alloy steels with a hardness of 700–1000 N/mm²	N/GT 100	HSS	118°	12 – 16	3	Soluble oil
Alloyed tool steels hardness 800–1000 N/mm² and refined alloy steels with a hardness of 1000–1200 N/mm₂	N/GV	HSCO (HSS)	118° (130°)	10 – 16	2	Soluble oil
Refined alloy steels with a hardness of > 1200 N/mm²	N/GV	HSCO	130°	5 – 8	1	Soluble oil, cutting oil
Chrome-molybdenum, stainless steel	N	HSCO	130°	8 – 12	1	Soluble oil, cutting oil
Stainless, austenitic, nickel-chrome, heat resisting steels	N/Ti (Specials)	HSCO	130°	3 – 8	1	Cutting oil or cutting oil with molybdenum disulphide additives
Manganese steels containing up to 10% molybdenum	H (Specials)	HSCO	130°	3 – 5	1	Dry: preheat to 200°–300°
Spring steels	N/GV	HSCO (HSS)	130°	5 – 10	1	Soluble oil, cutting oil
Nimonic alloys	W/Ti (Specials)	HSCO	130°	3 – 8	1	Cutting oil or cutting oil with molybdenum disulphide additives
Ferro-tic	N/Ti	HSCO	118°/130°	3 – 5	1	Dry: compressed air
Titanium and titanium alloys	Ti (Specials)	HSCO	130°	3 – 5	1	Cutting oil or cutting oil with molybdenum disulphide additives
Grey cast iron up to GG 26 and malleable iron	N	HSS (HSCO) (double angle point)	118°/90°	16 – 25	5	Dry: soluble oil
Hard cast iron up to 350 brinell	N	HSCO (double angle point)	118°/90°	8 – 12	4	Dry: soluble oil
Brass to MS 58	H	HSS	118°	60 – 80	6	Dry: cutting oil
Brass from MS 60	H (N)	HSS	118°	30 – 60	5	Soluble oil, cutting oil
Red copper	W/GT 50	HSS	130°	30 – 60	5	Soluble oil, cutting oil

Cutting data for drilling (contd.)

Material of workpiece	Drill type	Material of drill	Point angle	Cutting speed m per min.	Feed scale No. (see Fig.A4.1)	Coolant
Electrolytic copper	N	HSS	130°	20 – 30	5	Soluble oil, cutting oil
German silver	N	HSS	118°	20 – 30	3	Soluble oil, cutting oil
Copper nickel and copper-tin alloys	N	HSS	130°	20 – 30	3	Soluble oil, cutting oil
Copper-aluminium alloys	N	HSS	130°	10 – 30	3	Soluble oil, cutting oil
Alloys of copper and beryllium	H	HSS	130°	10 – 16	2	Soluble oil, cutting oil
Copper-manganese and copper-silicon alloys	N	HSS	130°	25 – 30	3	Soluble oil, cutting oil
Pure aluminium	W/GT 50	HSS	130°	40 – 60	5	Soluble oil
Aluminium-manganese and aluminium-chrome alloys	W/GT 50	HSS	130°	40 – 60	5	Soluble oil
Aluminium alloyed with lead, antimony or tin	W/GT 50	HSS	130°	60 –100	5	Soluble oil
Aluminium-copper alloys containing silicon, magnesium, lead, tin, titanium or beryllium	W/GT 50	HSS	130°	40 – 60	5	Soluble oil
Aluminium-silicon alloys containing copper, magnesium, manganese or chrome	W/GT 50	HSS	130°	40 – 60	5	Soluble oil
Aluminium-magnesium alloys with silicon, manganese or chrome	W/GT 50	HSS	130°	60 –100	5	Soluble oil
Magnesium and magnesium alloys (Electron)	W/GT 50	HSS	130°	80 –100	5	Dry
Zinc, Zamac	N	HSS	118°	30 – 40	4	Soluble oil
Hard duroplastics	H	HSS/HM	80°	10-20/50-100	3/4	Dry: Compressed air
Soft thermoplastics	W/GT 50	HSS	130°	16 – 40	3	Water: Compressed air
Hardboard and the like	W/H*	HSS	130°	16 – 25	3	Dry: Compressed air
Eternit, slate, marble	H	HSS (HM)	80°	3 – 5	from hand	Dry: Compressed air
Graphite	N	HSS (HM)	80°	3 – 5	from hand	Dry: Compressed air
Ebonite, Vulcanite	H	HSS	80°	16 – 30	6	Dry: Compressed air
Perspex	H	HSS	130°	16 – 25	3	Water

*) W = Drilling in the direction of the layers
H = Drilling at right angles to the layers

N.B. The foregoing recommendations hold good only if the following conditions are met with:

a) uniform consistency of the material to be drilled;
b) drills are to B.S. 328 and DIN 338;
c) Guhring drills of HSS and HSCO quality are used;
d) maximum depth does not exceed 3 times the drill diameter;
e) good machine condition and rigid mounting of the workpiece;
f) no drilling bushes are used;
g) correct quality of coolant and sufficient flow;
h) no excessive run-out of the machine spindle or drill.

Bearing these points in mind the figures in the tables may be increased or reduced accordingly.

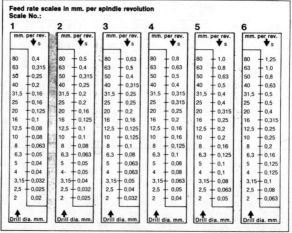

Fig.A4.1

APPENDIX 5

Isometric Thread Data

Course pitch series (preferred sizes)

Major diameter	Pitch	Minor diameters		Drill sizes	
		Screw	Nut	Tapping	Clearance
2	0.4	1.509	1.567	1.6	2.4
2.5	0.45	1.948	2.013	2.05	2.9
3	0.5	2.387	2.459	2.5	3.4
4	0.7	3.141	3.242	3.3	4.5
5	0.8	4.01	4.134	4.2	5.5
6	1	4.773	4.918	5	6.6
8	1.25	6.466	6.467	6.8	9
10	1.5	8.160	8.376	8.5	11
12	1.75	9.853	10.016	10.2	14
16	2	13.546	13.835	14	18
20	2.5	16.933	17.294	17.5	22
24	3	20.319	20.752	21	26
30	3.5	25.706	26.211	26.5	33

APPENDIX 6

Geometric tolerances

Geometrical tolerance symbols

SYMBOL	CHARACTERISTIC	APPLICATION
——	STRAIGHTNESS	Applied to an edge line or axis. For an edge or line the tolerance zone is the area between two parallel straight lines containing the edge or line. The tolerance value is the distance between the two lines.
▱	FLATNESS	Applied to a surface. The tolerance zone is the space between two parallel planes. The tolerance value is the distance between the two planes.
○	ROUNDNESS	Applied to the cross-section of a cylinder, cone or sphere. The tolerance zone is the annular space between two concentric circles lying in the same plane. The tolerance value is the distance between the two circles.
⌀	CYLINDRICITY	Applied to the surface of a cylinder. Combines roundness, straightness and parallelism. The tolerance zone is the annular space between two coaxial cylinders. The tolerance zone is the radial distance between the two cylinders.
⌒	PROFILE OF A LINE	Applied to a profile. The tolerance zone is an area defined by two lines that have a constant width normal to the stated profile. The tolerance is the diameter of a series of circles contained between the two lines. The tolerance may be unilateral or bilateral.
⌓	PROFILE OF A SURFACE	Applied to a surface. The tolerance zone is a space contained between two surfaces normal to the stated surface. The tolerance value is the diameter of a series of spheres enveloped by the two surfaces. The tolerance may be unilateral or bilateral.
//	PARALLELISM	Applied to a line, surface or cylinder. The tolerance zone is the area between two parallel lines or planes, or the space between two parallel cylinders, which must be parallel to the datum feature. The tolerance is the distance between the two lines or planes or, in the case of a cylinder, the diameter of the cylinder.
⊥	SQUARENESS	Applied to a line, surface or cylinder. For a line or surface the tolerance zone is the area between two parallel lines or planes which are perpendicular to the datum surface. The tolerance is the distance between the lines or planes. For a cylinder the tolerance zone is the space within a cylinder equal in diameter to the tolerance value and perpendicular to the datum plane.
∠	ANGULARITY	Applied to a line, surface or cylinder. For a line or surface the tolerance is the area or space between two parallel lines or planes inclined at a specified angle to the datum feature. For a cylinder the tolerance zone is the space within a cylinder equal in diameter to the tolerance value and inclined at a specified angle to the datum feature.
⊕	POSITION	Applied to a circle or cylinder. The tolerance zone is the space within a cylinder equal in diameter to the tolerance value and coaxial with the datum axis. The tolerance limits the deviation of the datum axis from its true position.
◎	CONCENTRICITY	Applied to parallel lines or surfaces. The tolerance zone is the area of space between the lines or surfaces symmetrically disposed in relation to a datum feature. The tolerance value is the distance between the lines or planes.
≡	SYMMETRY	Applied to a point, axis, line or plane. The tolerance zone definition varies according to the feature. The tolerance value will limit the positional deviation from the specified true position.
↗	RUN OUT	Applied to the surface of a solid of revolution or to a face perpendicular to the axis. The tolerance value indicates the permissible indicator movement during one revolution.
Ⓜ	MAXIMUM MATERIAL CONDITION	MMC exists when the component or feature contains the maximum amount of material permitted by its dimensional tolerances. When M is included in a tolerance frame the tolerance value need only be applied rigorously when the component or feature is in that condition. When not in that condition the geometric tolerance may be increased up to the difference between the MMC limit and the actual finished size.

APPENDIX 6.2

Geometric tolerance frames

1. Tolerance relating to a single datum:

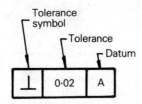

2. Tolerance relating to more than one datum:

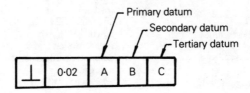

3. Datums to which tolerances are noted elsewhere are indicated as follows:

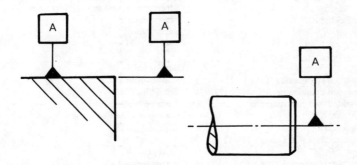

Examples of geometric tolerances are included on the detail drawings on pages 154, 159, 160, 163 and 165.

Further information relating to geometric tolerances may be obtained by reference to BS 308 Part III.

INDEX